MW00836813

The Time Museum
Catalogue of the Collection

Catalogue of the Collection

General Editor: Bruce Chandler

The Time

Museum

Volume I
Time Measuring Instruments

Part 3
Water-clocks
Sand-glasses
Fire-clocks

by A.J. Turner

Rockford 1984

THE TIME MUSEUM
Director: Seth G. Atwood
Curator: William Andrewes

Coordinated by
William Andrewes

Photographs by
Douglas Hamm
Stephen Pitkin

Designed by
Lucy Sisman
Richard Weigand

Typeset by
Talbot Typographics, Inc.

Printed by
h.c. Johnson Press

ISBN 0–912947–01–2
ISSN 0737–3546
©The Time Museum, 1984

Introduction

Collecting does not, by any means, involve objects alone. In fact, my strongest recollections are of people and places, and these invoke thousands of pleasant memories. As an example, in this introduction I will relate the story of the acquisition of one of the pieces described in this catalogue.

First let me explain that The Time Museum only displays reproductions when they represent important developments in the history of timekeeping devices and the originals are unobtainable. The astronomical clock tower of Su Song (catalogue no. 5) is such an object: It was one of the first documented artifacts to divide a force into discrete intervals of time, yet the original is no longer in existence, having been destroyed centuries ago. In quest of material concerning Su Song's tower, in the early 1970's I visited Derek de Solla Price, Avalon Professor of the History of Science at Yale University, who, along with Wang Ling and Joseph Needham, wrote a book entitled *Heavenly Clockwork, the Great Astronomical Clocks of Medieval China*, which described this clock. It was a pleasant, sunny spring day that I went to Derek's office and we hit it off immediately. Derek was a born teacher and I was an eager pupil full of questions. The texture and scope of his answers didn't cease to astound me. With his unconventional wisdom, Derek had a natural ability to inspire research by interjecting remarks which questioned accepted history. My afternoon visit extended through to dinner and I wound up spending the night. Derek and I subsequently had occasion to see each other many times in Europe, Canada, and the U.S. until his death, in the fall of 1983. My calendar reads "Dinner with Derek — History of Science annual meeting — October 29, Norwalk, Connecticut" — a dinner which thus sadly never took place.

Following my visit to Derek in 1970, the trail led to John Combridge in England, who had built a model of the clock. After numerous telephone calls, reaching him resulted in a gracious invitation to his home in Essex. I arrived in time for tea and rapport was quickly established because Mrs. Combridge's maiden name was Attwood! We were both aware of our English heritage, which suggests a common ancestry: a William Attewode, who in 1278 settled on a forty-acre estate in Coulsdon Parish, Surrey. I told her the story of how my family and I had seen the great house of Sanderstead Court on this land in 1936, with the family coat-of-arms carved in stone above the main entrance. Sadly, this great house, parts of which dated back to the 15th century, and the rectory, were destroyed in World War II. However, the lovely little Sanderstead Church still stands, and many Attwoods, over many generations, are marked by tombstones surrounding the church.

Eventually we got around to discussing Su Song, and John Combridge showed me his small table models and the half-scale waterwheel which was running in a room adjacent to the kitchen. There was an electrical impulse drive to a homemade kitchen wall clock from this waterwheel, which, he stated, kept excellent time. John's knowledge was extensive. He had learned Chinese so as to read the early records, and had made dimensional drawings of the Su Song clock. Clearly the Su Song project was a labor of love.

John told me that one of the relevant books was in the British Museum and he also gave me the name and address of Barnett and Walls, the company that had constructed his model. He offered to supervise the construction of another model. This was more than hospitality!

The next morning found me at Barnett and Walls. I am always astounded by English craftsmanship; beautifully finished, long-lasting articles are painstakingly made at low cost. In due course, the waterwheel was made and shipped to Rockford.

My next stop was the British Museum, where I obtained a complete photocopy of the rare book on Su Song's clock. By now, I had committed myself to a reconstruction of the entire clock which, even at half-scale, would be 17½ feet tall.

Through Swiss connections, I found a tiny shop in the Black Forest, whose craftsmen carved 117 six-inch-high figures of Chinese people in traditional costume, holding various objects painted in a variety of colors. These were based on sketches roughly drawn by me, partly from text drawings and partly from imagination. The investigation as to how these figures should be designed was another pleasant side benefit of collecting.

Back in Rockford lay the task of building the rest of the clock. This typical Midwestern city of 140,000 people is 90 miles northwest of Chicago and is the second largest city in Illinois. By a typical Midwestern city, I mean that Rockford has a continual perception of the importance of the self-reliance and independence that was called for when small settlements sprang up in the early part of the 19th century. The Rock River, a relatively large river that empties into the Mississippi, bisects the city, with its many parks, rolling hills, and well-kept homes. A wave of Scandinavian people settled in

Rockford, and brought with them a pride in quality and handwork, particularly woodworking.

Yousta Johnson, one of the 1,585 Johnsons in the telephone book, and a fine woodcarver, hand-carved three half-lifesize Chinese figures. He also made a globe for the second floor of the clock and an armillary sphere for the third floor. Many nights and weekends in his basement were involved, since he worked during the day full-time as a pattern maker.

Sofus Sorensen is a first-rate cabinet maker of Danish descent, who works alone in the well-equipped shop attached to his home. Except for the waterwheel and the work Yousta did, Sofus built all the rest of the Su Song reconstruction — a beautiful job, in solid teak.

This project took about four years, off and on, and we still need to make some of the wooden gears. About six years ago, Sofus thought that he would retire. Fortunately, however, his idea of retirement never worked out. The museum has become his second home, and he continues to make cabinets and displays, in never-ending succession, with pride and a total dedication to quality.

This story of the reconstruction of the Su Song clock is an example of how collecting is more than the mere accumulation of objects. New friends, new places, and new experiences — these are some of the personal rewards which lie behind the artifacts displayed.

SETH G. ATWOOD

Rockford, November 1983

Foreword

This volume of the general catalogue of The Time Museum, Rockford, Illinois is the third of those which describe all the time-finding and measuring instruments in the collection which are not clocks or watches in the accepted sense of the word – that is, geared movements driven by weights, springs, or electricity. The volumes which together make up Volume I of the whole catalogue include:

1. Astrolabes
   Horizontal Instruments
   Astrolabe-quadrants

2. Sundials
   Nocturnals

3. Water-clocks
   Sand-glasses
   Fire-clocks

4. Calendars
   Astronomical and Other Instruments

Each volume although part of the set is complete in itself with its own bibliography and index. A narrative history of the development of each class of instrument included in the collection has been provided since no general synthesis of the history of time-measuring instruments seems to exist in English. These sections, therefore, may be read continuously as an introduction to the subject. Descriptions of individual items in the collection are arranged as nearly as possible in chronological order. Where there are several items of the same date, they are arranged in alphabetical order of the maker's name (if known) or that of the region of origin. Technical details are then given in the following order:

1. Object.

2. Date. Where an object is dated in a calendar system other than that of the Christian era, the date as marked on the instrument is given first, and its European equivalent, indicated by the initials A.D., is shown in brackets immediately after it. Dates in the Islamic Hijra are indicated by the letters A.H.[1]

3. Materials.

4. Overall key dimensions, in inches and millimetres.

5. Signature transcribed or transliterated with contractions ex-

---

1. These have been converted following the tables in Freeman-Grenville. For other calendars used in the countries of Islam, see Taqizadeh.

panded and translated where necessary. Transliterations of Arabic signatures follow the form adopted by L.A. Mayer, and in the forthcoming revision of this work.[2] Transliterations of Chinese signatures are in pinyin.[3] An enlarged photograph of the signature or inscription follows each transcription or translation.

6. Museum inventory number (which should be cited in any communication with the museum about the item).

7. General description of the object, method of use, and commentary.

8. Provenance, when known.

9. Biographical notes on the maker, where possible.

In compiling this catalogue, of a collection which covers many centuries and widely dispersed civilizations, I have inevitably been heavily dependent upon the published works of others, and on the kindnesses of colleagues. Bibliographical references in the footnotes, and the list of acknowledgments below, can in some measure show the extent of my indebtedness and express my gratitude; they do not excuse faults which remain. Particularly I wish to acknowledge my indebtedness to Seth G. Atwood, and to thank William Andrewes, Curator, and Jan Dolman, Assistant Curator, of The Time Museum for their aid. From the General Editor, Bruce Chandler, flowed much valuable comment, criticism, and hospitality, which have greatly enhanced the volume. The explanatory diagrams were specially drawn for the work by David Penney, and the indexes were prepared by Jennifer Drake-Brockman. For help in many ways, scholarly and administrative, I am grateful to David Bailey, London; Silvio A. Bedini, Washington, D.C.; Alain Brieux, Paris; Giuseppe Brusa, Milan; Catherine Cardinal, Paris; John Combridge, Ilford; Richard Good, London; Donald Hill, Great Bookham; Beresford Hutchinson, Greenwich; Dione Johnson, London; John Leopold, Groningen; Francis Maddison, Oxford; Philip Rogers, London; George Saliba, New York; Mary Tregear, Oxford; Roderick and Marjorie Webster, Winnetka; Susan Youngs, London.

The source of illustrations is given at the end of each caption and grateful acknowledgment is here made to all the institutions that have supplied photographs. Uncredited illustrations are from the collections of The Time Museum.

A.J.T.

Le Mesnil-le-Roi, France

December, 1981

2. Mayer (I & II) and Brieux & Maddison. I am indebted to Alain Brieux and Francis Maddison for providing much information from this work in advance of publication, and for transliterations and translations of inscriptions on Islamic instruments.
3. I am indebted to Carole Morgan, Paris, for transliteration from the Chinese.

Contents

Water-clocks

Water-clocks

L'humidité, Hydraule de mes yeulx,
Vuyde tousiours par l'impie en l'oblique,
L'y attrayant, pour air des vuydes lieux,
Ces miens souspirs, qu'a suyure elle s'applique.
  Ainsi tous temps descent, monte, et replique [,]
Pour abreuer mes flammes appaisées.
  Doncques me sont mes larmes si aisées
A tant pleurer, que sans cesser distillent?
Las du plus (,) hault goutte a goutte elles filent,
Tombant aux sains, dont elles sont puysées.

Maurice Scève, *Délie, Objet de plus haulte vertu*
(1544), cccxxxi[1]

(Moisture, a clepsydra running from my eyes,
thanks to the pitiless one [lack of pity] flows
  always in a circle,
drawn there like air into a vacuum
by these sighs of mine, which it hastens to follow.
So, all the time, [my tears] fall, rise, and repeat
  [the cycle]
to drench and so quieten my ardour.
Is it so easy to cry so much that my tears fall
  one by one without cease?
Alas, from the highest point, drop by drop, they
  course down,
falling on my breast whence they are drawn.)

Water-clocks (clepsydrae) are perhaps the oldest of all time-measuring instruments.[2] In consequence, the date and place of their first appearance are unknown and probably unknowable. Attested to in ancient Babylon before the 16th century B.C.,[3] a clepsydra is mentioned in Egypt in an XVIIIth dynasty (16th century B.C.) inscription on the tomb of an official, Amenemhet at Shaikh Abd al-Gurna.[4] The earliest archaeological fragments surviving are those of the clepsydra found at the temple of Karnak in Upper Egypt (fig. 23). These date from the reign of King Amenhotep III (1415 –1380 B.C.).[5] Thereafter we have a fragmentary series of references, documents, and artifacts which extend through four millennia to modern times.

With few exceptions, clepsydrae may be classified into one of four basic groups: outflow clepsydrae, inflow clepsydrae, continuous-flow scoop-wheel clepsydrae, and compartmented cylinder clepsydrae. All ancient clepsydrae belong to the first two groups.

1. The text follows that given by McFarlane, 300. Although not stated explicitly to apply to a water-clock, this stanza very well describes the thermodynamic cycle of the instrument. That the analogy was in the poet's mind is suggested by his use of 'Hydraule' (which is capitalized) in line 1, and 'distillent' in line 8. Both these terms are used in the context of a clepsydra in Scève's long poem *Microcosme* (1562), III, 703. 'L'Hydraule vint apres qui le tems distilloit.' As McFarlane has pointed out, however, the dizaine also depends upon 'the old theory of the physiology of tears. Tears were believed to well up from the heart, and then to pass through the eyes, they then fell upon the heart or chest, thus coming full circle' (456). We may wonder if this idea is not also hinted at in Perrault's reconstruction of Ctesibios' clepsydra as described by Vitruvius (cat. no. 4). For drawing my attention to the stanza in *Délie* I am grateful to Francis Maddison, and especially to Gillian Downing, who exhumed the poem from R.P.H. Gasser & W.G. Richards, *Entropy and Energy Levels,* Oxford, 1974, 120, and by whom the resemblance to the operational cycle of a clepsydra was noted.
2. The only possible exceptions are the vertical gnomon and day-counting tally sticks.
3. See Neugebauer (I). For a more extensive survey of the clepsydra in antiquity than that which follows, see Schmidt, which remains useful despite its age.
4. Translated and discussed by Sloley, 45.
5. See cat. no. 1. It is fully described by Borchardt in the most detailed study of Egyptian time measurement. A list of twelve other fragments of water-clocks known to Borchardt is given (7–10) with reconstructions where possible. A further fragment is discussed by Capart and a further unpublished example exists in the Oriental Institute, Chicago.

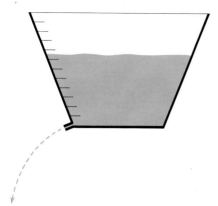

figure 1. Principle of the outflow clepsydra.

Outflow Clepsydrae

At their simplest, clepsydrae of the first group consist of a vessel graduated on the inside and with a small hole at the bottom. The vessel is filled with water, and as it gradually drips away, the hour may be determined by the level of the water against the graduated scale (fig. 1). The origin of the device is unknown, but at an early date two fundamental developments took place. Firstly, an attempt was made to equalize the rate of flow of the water, which varied with the decrease in pressure as the height of the water above the orifice fell. This was done by inclining the sides so that the diameter at the brim was twice that at the base, thus producing a truncated cone. This step had been taken at least by the end of the 16th century B.C. in Egypt,[6] and probably earlier. Secondly, attempts were made to accommodate the clepsydra to the unequal-hour system (see Appendix) of the ancient world, which posed a problem since adjustments had to be made regularly to the clepsydra as the seasons changed. In Babylon this seems to have been overcome by varying the amount of water with which the clepsydra was charged. Calculations of the weight of the requisite quantity of water have survived in a number of cuneiform texts.[7] In Egypt the problem was resolved by marking twelve separate hour scales, one for each month, on the inner wall, each differently graduated. An inscription of Amenemhet c. 1580 B.C. possibly records the moment when this was first done; at the least it takes us back to a period when knowledge of the phenomenon was evidently not widespread.[8] The instrument that resulted from these two developments seems to have been reasonably effective. Recent experiments with a facsimile of the Karnak clepsydra suggest that it had an average error of about ten minutes, a figure which agrees well with that of twelve minutes deduced from an analysis of observations recorded by Ptolemy as having been made with a clepsydra.[9]

The development of the outflow clepsydra, if any, in the succeed-

6. E.g. the Karnak clepsydra (cat. no. 1) is of this form.
7. In particular the series known as the *Mul Apin* texts (*c.* 687 B.C. or earlier). See Neugebauer (I), *passim.* Thureau-Dangin discusses the texts of B.M. 85194 & 85210.
8. The inscription, which is fragmentary, reads in part (in Sloley's reconstruction and translation), '. . .[I found that the winter night was] fourteen ['hours' long]. . .if the summer night was 12 "hours" [long]. . .[I found an increase in the length of the nights] from month to month [and] decrease month by month. . . I [represented] them on the vessel of the water clock and the movements of [the Sun god] Re. . . I made a *Mrhyt* reckoned from the zero of year [?] It was for the deceased king. . . Never was one made like it since the beginning of time. I made this splendid instrument in honour of the deceased king, Amenhotep I, divided in half [and thirds]. It was correct [?] at the beginning of the harvest season, in winter [?] at the. . .of the moon in its times. Every hour [lies] to its time [?]. The water runs out through one outlet only.' A facsimile of the inscription and a German translation may be found in Borchardt, 60–3. Since the odd quarter of a day in the length of a year was a neglected factor in the graduation of water-clocks, this graduation would, after 120 years, be exactly one month out of phase. By the Ptolemaic period this error had been detected, and examples of clepsydrae with the month names revised have survived. See Pogo, 411.
9. See Mackensen; Fotheringham, *passim.*

ing millennium is unknown. Knowledge of it did, however, become more widely spread (though whether by diffusion or by re-invention is impossible to say).[10] It may have reached China in the 7th century B.C.[11] and seems to have been transmitted from Mesopotamia to India, perhaps in the 6th/5th centuries B.C.[12] Certainly it was known in Athens in the 5th century B.C.[13] A surviving example of *c*. 400 B.C. recently excavated from a well on the Athenian Agora has no graduations.[14] For its purpose, however, this did not matter. The Agora clepsydra was a timer for the law courts, where its function (similar to that of the sand- or pulpit glass in 16th- and 17th-century A.D. European churches) was simply to measure a discrete interval of time. Of two *chous* capacity (6.4 litres) and marked with the name of the tribe which owned it, the Agora clepsydra would have been used for timing the second speech on each side in legal cases involving sums of money between 1,000 and 5,000 drachmas.[15] For measuring longer or shorter periods, clepsydrae of different capacities would have been used.

The law courts were not the only place where outflow clepsydrae could be used. An inscription from the island of Iasos indicates that they were used to regulate administrative assemblies. Each was capable of holding one *metretes* (μετρηταῖον = 12 χόες = approximately 9 English gallons), each had a hole 'the size of a bean' (τρύπημ εχον κναμιαῖον), and each was placed seven feet from the ground.[16] In military camps they were used for regulating the period of the watch. Thus, it was presumably because of the failure of the clepsydra period to coincide with the period of darkness that Julius Caesar discovered the nights to be shorter in Britain than on the mainland of Europe.[17] Similarly, in the mid-4th century B.C.,

10. For general accounts of clepsydrae in antiquity, see Schmidt, Bilfinger.
11. Needham & Wang Ling (I), 315. These references, however, are philologically somewhat uncertain and therefore may not be admitted as firm evidence. The earliest clear reference seems to be in a biography of the 6th-century B.C. general and politician Sima Zhangju, who while waiting for an appointment with another general 'set up a sundial and started the water-clock dripping.' Needham & Wang Ling (II), 479, n. c.
12. Discussion of the cylindrical outflow clepsydra in Laghoda's *Jyotisha-vedangā* (5th–4th centuries B.C.) and of the quantity of water to be used at different seasons has been linked with similar discussions in the *Mul Apin* texts, thus implying a transmission from Babylon. See Pingree, 3–4; Forbes, 150–60.
13. The earliest Greek reference to a clepsydra occurs in Aristophanes *Acharnians*, 693–4, *c*. 425 B.C. References to κλεψυδρα in Aristotle's *Physica* (213 a 25–28); *de Caelo* (270b 20); and *Problemata* (914 b 9) referring to Anaxagoras (*c*. 500–*c*. 430 B.C.) and his experiments on air pressure (see Gershenson & Greenberg, 66, 68, & 79) are not to water-clocks but to siphons, the instrument referred to being similar to a toddy-lifter (see Last; O'Brien, 168–9, 176–9). The same instrument was used by Empedocles, and classical examples have survived.
14. It is excellently described and set in context by Young. There are a number of minor differences from the Karnak example, i.e. the proportions are different, the Athens example had handles similar to those of a water pot, the sides flare slightly, and a narrow copper spout was provided for the outlet.
15. Young, 279. Aristotle *Athenesium Respublica*, 67: 2. 'Ten *Chous* are allowed for a case in which an amount of more than five-thousand drachma is involved, and three for the second speech on each side. When the amount is between one- and five-thousand drachmas, seven *Chous* are allowed for the first speech and two for the second; when it is less than one thousand, five and two.' Translation of F.G. Kenyon in Ross.
16. Hinks, 104 and 108. The date of this inscription in the period from the 4th to the 2nd centuries B.C. is uncertain.
17. *de Bello Gallico*: 5: 13.6. Since Caesar landed in the early summer, this is not altogether astonishing.

Aeneas Tacticus[18] suggested that in order to make the night watches equal all the year round, the inside of the clepsydra should be smeared with wax, which could be gradually scraped out as the nights grew longer, and re-applied as they shortened again.[19] Clearly, however, these clepsydrae were ungraduated, as were probably the clepsydrae used to time chariot races in Byzantine Constantinople. An object supposed by Henri Michel to be a portable clepsydra is also apparently ungraduated.[20] This is a flared pot somewhat resembling a vase, with a single handle at one side and a hole in the bottom close to the wall. Like the Mycenean vases found by Sir Arthur Evans at Cnossos, its decoration supposedly indicates its function. On the exterior of the vases are depictions of plants or flowers. On the outside of the putative clepsydra is a design which has been interpreted as water dripping from a clepsydra schematically shown. Possibly then the clepsydra dates from the earliest ages of Greek history.[21] If so, it has had a remarkably long history, for it could be to a portable clepsydra of this kind that Athenaeus (*fl.* A.D. 200) refers in a much-interpreted passage. Upbraiding a parsimonious man he says '. . . you carry about your jug from early morning, looking to see if there is oil in it; whence one would think that you carry about a water-clock (ὡρολογίον), and not a jug.'[22]

The association of outflow clepsydrae with domestic utensils also occurs in Northern India, where a primitive form of the instrument was in use at least by the end of the 4th century B.C.[23] This consisted of a water jar, or the lower half thereof, pierced with a carefully made hole of strictly prescribed proportions through which water dripped to measure one *nāḍī* (apparently 24 minutes). Mentioned unambiguously in texts of the 3rd century A.D., it continued in use after the introduction of the sinking-bowl water-clock[24] probably in the 4th century A.D. In 1915, fragments of a large royal outflow clepsydra dated A.D. 566–67 were recorded at Walā in Kāṭhiāwār.[25]

The clepsydra used in the Athenian law courts and elsewhere was not a timekeeper as was its Egyptian ancestor, but, like the sandglass which functionally it precedes, a measurer of only specific intervals of time. As such it was a more specialized instrument, but it was also a simpler one. About the reasons for this change we can, in the absence of evidence, only speculate, but it may be related to the

18. *Poliorcetica* (22:25), post 357 B.C.
19. Cited in Young, 277, n. 17 & 18.
20. Michel, *passim.* The object described was then in a private collection and its present location is unknown.
21. 'Selon certains specialistes, il pourrait dater du xiiiᵉ siècle avant notre ère,' *Ibid.,* 363.
22. Athenaeus, ch. iv: 163, ii. It is, however, easy to interpret this passage in other ways.
23. It is mentioned, although not fully described, in the *Jyotisha-vedangā* and the *Kautiliya-Arthasastra* both of *c.* 300 B.C. or earlier, Fleet, 213–30.
24. See below, p. 9.
25. Fleet, 230. It is not possible here to mention all later examples of the continuing use of the outflow clepsydra in China, Islam, North Africa, and Spain. We may, however, note that a perforated *noria* [? *recte, saqiya*] (i.e. water-wheel) pot was used for irrigation timing in North Africa. The method was described by al-Bakhrī at Touzer (Tunisia) in the 11th century A.D., and the same method could be seen in the same oasis at the beginning of the 20th century. See Glick, *passim.*

fact that the more complicated timekeeping and time-indicating functions of the Egyptian outflow clepsydra were carried out in the Greek world by instruments of a different pattern: inflow clepsydrae, the second of the four main groups.[26]

Inflow Clepsydrae

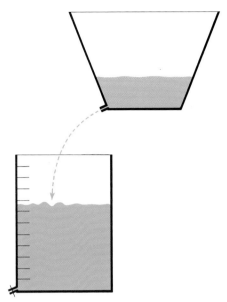

figure 2. Principle of the inflow clepsydra.

Reduced to its essentials, the inflow clepsydra consists simply of two tanks set one above the other. The upper tank is filled with water which pours slowly through a small hole into the second tank. Time is indicated by some kind of graduated scale associated with the receiving tank since it is the period taken to fill this tank that is measured (fig. 2). The origins of the device are obscure, but foundations interpreted as being those of a water-clock in the Athenian Agora (late 4th century B.C.) are perhaps those of an outflow clepsydra with a visual time signal, later converted to the inflow system.[27] In the 3rd century B.C. it was considerably developed by Ctesibios of Alexandria (*c.* 300–*c.* 230 B.C.). Ctesibios' work is discussed by Vitruvius (*fl.* 1st century B.C.) who, after listing the inventions and authors of descriptions of different kinds of sundials, says 'Methods of making water clocks have been investigated by the same writers, and first of all by Ctesibios the Alexandrian . . .'[28] Although this statement has been interpreted to mean that Ctesibios invented the inflow clepsydra, the Latin is ambiguous and there seems no reason to press the meaning so far. Ctesibios was evidently one of the leading mechanicians concerned with the water-clock, but Vitruvius makes it quite clear that there were others.

Two fundamental problems faced the constructors of inflow water-clocks: how to maintain a constant flow into the receiver, and how to indicate the unequal hours throughout the year. The solution to the first problem probably adopted by Alexandrian engineers was to add a supplementary overflow tank to the series between the supply tank and the receiver (fig. 3). This extra tank had an outlet set high up on one side, and so allowed the quantity of water within to remain constant. Thus the supply of water entering the receiver could be maintained at a constant pressure. Ctesibios used gold or a pierced gemstone for the orifices, which reduced problems that would otherwise have been caused by clogging and wear. To indicate the hours, a float was placed in the receiver with a rod attached (perhaps held in the hand of a small figure) to indicate the hour against a scale mounted above the receiver. To compensate for the

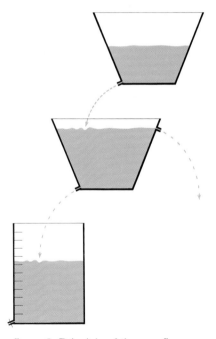

figure 3. Principle of the overflow tank.

26. A paper which supplies perhaps the most detailed available consideration of the behaviour of the outflow clepsydra unfortunately appeared after the present work was set up in type. See A.A. Mills, 'Newton's Water Clocks and the fluid mechanics of Clepsydrae,' *Notes and Records of the Royal Society of London,* 37, 1982, 35–61.
27. Armstrong & MckCamp, *passim,* which study came to my attention too late to be used fully in the present work; Lang, 30–1, pls. 43 & 44.
28. Vitruvius, IX, viii, 2. The most useful edition is that of Soubiran.

changing length of the hour throughout the year, either a system of wedges was used[29] or curved hour lines were projected onto a column with twelve vertical lines representing the twelve months. This column was made to revolve slowly so that hour spacings appropriate to the time of the year were presented to the marker (catalogue no. 4).[30]

Invention of this form of clepsydra – the 'parastatic clock,' as it may be called after Vitruvius[31] – is often ascribed to Ctesibios, and the form may be reasonably associated with him even if there is no clear evidence of the invention. Possibly, since they are specifically mentioned in relation with him by Vitruvius, we may ascribe to him the introduction of the gold orifice, and the float and marker. It is clear nonetheless that other forms of water-clocks which were not simply outflow clepsydrae preceded him. Both Plato (437–347 B.C.) and Aristotle (384–322 B.C.) are reported to have had 'alarm' clocks. That of Plato employed a siphon to produce a loud whistle;[32] Aristotle's perhaps utilized the fall of a hard ball into a brass basin.[33] Neither seems to have had any visual time indications, and Drachmann has suggested that aural time indication was characteristic of the earlier clocks,[34] visual time indication developing from the 3rd century B.C. onwards.

Certainly by the 3rd century B.C. a solid body of knowledge concerning pneumatics, hydraulics, and mechanics had been established and was growing.[35] Particularly at Alexandria, the city with which several of the few known mechanicians are associated, a tradition developed of ingenious water-clocks that drove complicated automata, mechanical toys, siphons, drinking-vessels, lamps, water-wheels, and pumps. Although in many cases these devices were simply the diversions of a leisured class, they embody many interesting mechanical ideas, established a tradition of mechanical investigation, and some at least were turned to practical use. We know the names of few of the practitioners of these skills. Of the work of Ctesibios, Philo (late 3rd/early 2nd century B.C.), Adronikos of Cyrrhos (*fl.* 1st century B.C.) and Hero of Alexandria (*fl.*

29. *Ibid.,* IX; viii, 6. The wedges held in place the plug of the valve which controlled the flow of water into the clepsydra. Each day the wedge was adjusted to give a larger or smaller flow aperture, thus decreasing or increasing the length of the hour.

30. *Ibid.,* IX; viii, 7. For detailed technical and historical discussion, see Drachmann (II). Soubiran, 270 ff; Gille (III), 97–101.

31. Vitruvius, IX; viii. We follow here the usage of Drachmann (II).

32. Diels (II), 198 ff. For the suggestion that Plato's philosophy was influenced by contemporary water-clocks and other hydraulic machines, and that the myth of cosmic reversal in particular supplies evidence for the existence of public clocks on the Agora, see Brumbaugh.

33. Moraux, *passim.*

34. Drachmann (II), 19. If so, then this would be an interesting parallel with the earliest mechanical clocks.

35. For a general survey of Hellenistic technology, see Drachmann (IV), and Gille (III). An example of minor development is provided by Hero's siphon-carrying float, which ensured a constant flow of water and could be adjusted for the daily change in the length of the hour by means of a screw. This apparatus, when it reappears in an edition of Hero's work by an anonymous reviser usually known as pseudo-Hero (? 6th century A.D.), has been further improved by the addition of a second siphon guide. Pseudo-Hero's text may also provide the first mention of a small screw-nut in ancient literature. See Drachmann (I).

A.D. 50–65), some fragments remain. Of the inventors of sundials whom Vitruvius lists and associates with those who made water-clocks and other devices, nothing at all is known. Vitruvius himself may be added to the list, as may Archimedes, to whom a long tradition in Arabic literature persisted in ascribing a water-clock.[36] Pappus (A.D. 4th century) is perhaps a late representative of the school, also at Alexandria. There must, however, have been many more such men. The technology of Hellenistic Greece, like its mathematics and physics, was subtle and sophisticated. The centuries from 100 B.C. to A.D. 100 saw the appearance of the anaphoric clock,[37] the remarkable celestial calculator known as the Antikythera machine,[38] forms of mechanical celestial models,[39] and at least one monumental public astronomical clock.[40] All this amounts to a considerable body of technical innovation which has left behind a few archaeological fragments and virtually no literary evidence. Technology was, however, an important element in Hellenistic civilization and the transmission of this technology to Rome, to the Byzantine Empire, to barbarian Europe, and to Islam, made up a crucial part of the Classical inheritance.

According to Pliny,[41] the first water-clock was erected in Rome by Scipio Nasica in 159 B.C. Unfortunately he gives no details and we do not know what type it was, or how it marked the hours–whether visually or aurally. That knowledge of the instrument derived from Greece is highly probable, and the Greek use of the outflow clepsydra to time disputations and legal proceedings was similarly taken over in Rome,[42] as were such *parerga* of the water-clocks as trumpeters, whistles, and celestial indications. Cicero, besides mentioning clocks and sketches of clocks[43] in his writings, is known

36. The fact, pointed out by Drachmann (II), 36, that there is no evidence anywhere in *surviving* classical literature concerning Archimedes' clock need not be considered conclusive argument against his having built, or at the least designed, one. For Arabic treatises ascribed to Archimedes, see below, n. 101.
37. For the anaphoric clock, see Vitruvius IX; 8–10; Drachmann (II), 21 ff; Soubiran, 290 ff. Basically it consisted of a water-clock which turned a disc on which were painted the signs of the zodiac and a number of stars behind a fixed grill representing the hours and the observer's local coordinates (see figs. 13 & 14). For the possible relationship of the device with the astrolabe, see Drachmann (III), *passim*.
38. The most recent study is by Price (III). For a reconstruction of the machine, see Volume I, part 4 of this catalogue.
39. E.g. those of Cicero in *de Republica* I, xiv & *Tusculan Disputationes* I. 63; *de Natura Deorum* II, xxxiv–xxxv.
40. The clock was contained in the Tower of the Winds at Athens, built by Andronikos of Cyrrhos not later than 37 B.C. For the tower, see Stuart & Revett, I, 13–25 & pls. i–xix, and Robinson. For a reconstruction of the clock, see Noble & Price.
41. *Historia Naturalis,* VII, 60.213 '. . . Scipio Nasica collega Laenatis primus aqua divisit horas aeque noctium ac dierum, idque horologium sub tecto dicavit anno urbis DXCV' (Scipio Nasica, the colleague of Laenas, for the first time divided the hours both of day and night by water, and dedicated this clock [horologium] under his roof in the year of the city 595 [159 B.C.]).
42. E.g. Cicero, *de Oratore* III: 34.138 & *Tusculan Disputationes,* II: 27.67. Pliny the younger *Epis,* 2.11.14; 6.2.5; Martial, *Epigramata,* 6, 35. There must, however, have been some correlation with everyday time measurement since Roman judiciary periods seem to have been measured in solar hours. See Ardaillon, 261 and Marquardt, ii, 461, who also list with references other uses of the clepsydra in the Roman world.
43. For celestial indications Cicero, *de Natura Deorum,* II: xxxviii.97 'An cum machinatione quadam moveri aliquid videmus, ut sphaeram ut horas ut alia permulta, non dubitamus quin illa opera sint rationis . . .' (nor when we see something being moved by some mechanism, such as a globe or a clock or very many other things, should we doubt that those are works of reason). For sketches of clocks, *Ibid.,* II, 34.87.

to have possessed water-driven astronomical models, and by the beginning of the Christian era, it seems reasonable to believe that water-clocks were relatively well-known and fairly widely distributed. Although possession of an elaborate water-clock could still provide satirists in the 1st century A.D. with an image of ostentatious luxury,[44] it seems clear that water-clocks ranging from simple alarms to more elaborate devices driving automata or celestial models were available and bought by the wealthy leisured and ruling classes throughout the Hellenistic period and cultural area, and that a number of monumental public clocks were erected. Indeed, although little is known about them, there is some evidence for the existence of a small number of professional clock-makers (*clepsydrarii*).[45] Since the Hellenistic cultural area may be considered more or less coterminous in space, though not in time, with the Roman Empire, it is not astonishing to find water-clocks and powered automatic devices showing similarities with Greek models in disparate areas of Asia Minor such as Syria and Persia, and in Western Europe. Equally, it is not unjustifiable to see a crucial Hellenistic influence in the development of the important clock-making traditions of Europe, Islam, and perhaps even China.

From the early centuries of the Christian era a few artifacts and literary remains survive to provide some idea of the technological level of the period. The most important both in its size and for its influence in Islam and Europe is the collection of working notes and drafts which make up Hero's *Pneumatica*[46] (1st century A.D.). From approximately the same period there are remains of a clepsydra found at Edfu.[47] Lucian provides contemporary literary reference to a water-driven instrument that indicated time both aurally and visually,[48] while the wry remark of Seneca–'I cannot tell you the time for sure since it is easier to find agreement between philosophers than between clocks...'[49]–suggests that many of them existed. Far more substantial is the description given by Galen (*c.* A.D. 130–*c.* 200) of an inflow clepsydra made of a transparent substance with a scale of hours scratched on the exterior. The level of the water within indicated the time.[50] Third-century calculations for the size and quantity of water required in an outflow clepsydra survive in

44. *The Satyricon* ascribed to Petronius (before A.D. 65) II: xxvi. 'What? says he, don't you know at whose house it is today? Why the millionaire Trimalchio's! There's a clock in his dining-room with a trumpeter complete so that he can know at any moment how much older he's getting.'
45. Ardaillon, 264. Marquardt, ii, 467, n. 1.
46. Heronis Alexandrini, *Opera quae supersunt omnia* (5 vols.), Leipzig, 1899–1914, vol.I (ed. W. Schmidt), 1–492.
47. See cat. no. 2 below.
48. *Hippias* VIII. '...and the admirable Hippas showed us this work which had all the virtues of a bath... and it had two devices for showing the time, one by means of water and roaring, the other displaying it by means of the sun.' The last phrase may perhaps suggest something resembling an anaphoric clock (see above, n. 37) dial.
49. *Apocolocyntosis* 2:2. 'Horam non possum certam tibi dicere, facilius inter philosophos quam inter horologia conveniet.'
50. Marquardt, ii, 463–4; for the text from Περὶ διαγνωσεως, see Sauppe.

the Oxyrynchus papyrus,[51] and possession of an elaborate water-driven astronomical model is ascribed to Sapor, King of Persia. Here there may have been an independent tradition of clock-making, for in his much later (A.H. 60J/A.D. 1203–4) account of the clock built by his father, the Syrian engineer Ridwān says that a Persian called Hormuz had developed the basic Greek water-clock mechanism. 'That [design],' he adds, 'continued in the land of *Fārs* [Persia] for a long time, and was transmitted from there to the land of the Greeks, and its construction spread out in the land until it was transmitted to Damascus, where it was constructed up to the days of the Byzantines...'[52] Towards the end of the 3rd century, St. Sebastian and Polycarp were seeking the destruction of an elaborate glass astronomical model belonging to Chromatius, although this was not certainly water-powered.[53] Devices such as these presumably were made by highly-skilled artisans working in the tradition of Hero, perhaps in association with a philosopher-designer. Of these *mechanoi* (mechanicians), Pappus[54] offers us a glimpse, but apart from this indication of their existence we know little about them. For the period up to *c.* A.D. 500, detailed information is available for only one clock, that at Gaza, which incorporated automata simulating the labours of Hercules. It was described by Procopius[55] in *c.* A.D. 510. Although we have little detail – or even very precise information – about these objects, knowledge of their existence helps to suggest something of the distribution of water-clocks, astronomical models, and related devices. It also demonstrates the continuing liveliness of the Hellenistic tradition.

Sinking-bowl Water-clocks

While in the Hellenistic cultural region the inflow clepsydra was developing into a sophisticated instrument, time measurement elsewhere, China and Persia apart, depended on more primitive devices. One such, the sinking-bowl water-clock, is an inverse variant of the inflow clepsydra in which water flows into an empty vessel floating on a reservoir, through a small hole in its base (catalogue no. 3 & fig. 4). When it is full, the vessel sinks with a gurgling sound sufficient to attract the attention of an attendant who thereupon gives some form of aural time signal. The origin of the device

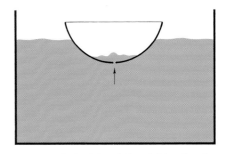

figure 4. Principle of the sinking-bowl clepsydra.

51. Grenfell & Hunt, no. 470. 11, 31–87.

52. Cited from Hill (VI). I am indebted to Dr. Hill for allowing me to use a typescript of this work before publication. For Sapor, see Planchon, 20, citing from Jerome Cardan.

53. The model was made for Chromatius' father, Tarquin, and consisted of a glass chamber with stellar, calendrical, lunar, and other astronomical indications. See Beckmann, i, 341. The history of clockwork, included in this work, and still one of the best surveys of the subject, was written by Georg Christoph Hamberger and read to a learned society at Göttingen in 1758. It was not, however, published until Beckmann incorporated it in his book.

54. *Collectio* VIII, Preface (*c.* A.D. 330). The passage is translated and discussed by Downey (I), 197–200.

55. εχφρασις 'ορωλογιον, edited with a German translation by Diels (I).

is unknown. The earliest literary reference to it occurs in Hindu works of *c.* A.D. 550[56] and in the *Surya Siddhanta*[57] (A.D. ?5th/6th century), the instrument itself being apparently an innovation of the mid-4th century or a little earlier. Although this might imply an Indian, or at least Asian origin, independent invention of it has been claimed for northwest Europe (probably in Britain) on the basis of several bronze vessels with perforated bottoms, which date from the late Iron Age.[58] Most of these vessels, however, are more readily explainable as laundry coppers, or cauldrons for culinary purposes.[59] Certainly the majority of them appear far too unstable to float without external support, and only examples of a flattened concave form really require consideration as water-clocks. The survival of at least two examples of this type – one from an Anglo-Saxon site, the other of indeterminate date[60] – suggest that the sinking-bowl water-clock may have existed in medieval Britain. That it originated there, or even in Europe, however, seems unlikely.

From India in the 4th/5th centuries the sinking-bowl water-clock appears to have spread widely through central Asia, where it continued in use virtually until the present day. In India itself it became the commonest form of timekeeper although in the 6th century it was only one of several. A description of its specifications is given in the *Surya Siddhanta*[61] and it was mentioned in the 10th century by al-Bīrūnī and by al-Muqaddasī.[62] Generally, however, it seems that the sinking-bowl instrument was uncommon in the heartlands of Islam.[63] Certainly it was a novelty to the first Mughal Emperor and conqueror of India, Babur,[64] and there are very few references to it in Islamic texts.

A similar situation prevailed in China, where although the device was certainly known – at some time in the Tang dynasty (A.D. 618–906) Hui Yuan arranged a series of twelve lotus-shaped bowls

56. Fleet, 213–30.
57. Burgess, ch. xiii, 23. There is, however, some possibility that this section of the work is a later interpolation.
58. See Smith, (I & II). Smith (III), 162–4.
59. See Hulme (I), rejoinder in Smith (IV) and reply to the rejoinder in Hulme (II) 213–15. The only important objection which Hulme did not satisfactorily resolve was 'why the hole in the bottom?' This may be explained as the result of the vessel's having been held in a lathe while worked, causing at least a depression in the metal which later wore into a hole, or at worst causing a hole which was afterwards plugged with lead or another metal. This suggestion was first made by Mr. Bushe-Fox (*Proc. Soc. Antiquaries,* 2nd ser., xxii, 1915, 94–5) in discussion of Smith's paper, when Fox pointed out the considerable differences in the size and state of the holes which Smith wished to consider as consciously made orifices.
60. These are: 1)A perforated saucer-shaped vessel of 4-inch diameter found in an Anglo-Saxon site at Market Overton, Rutland, inside a clay vessel the bottom of which it fitted precisely. In ten trial sinkings it took an average of 62 minutes 54 seconds to sink within a range of 56–72 minutes (*Proc. Soc. Antiquaries,* 2nd ser., xxii, 1907–09, 53). 2) A bowl of 9-inch diameter, now in the Museum of the History of Science, Oxford, which was found at Lakenheath Fen, Norfolk, during construction of the London–Norwich railway.
61. Burgess, 308.
62. By al-Bīrūnī as a homemade substitute for some other form of water-clock, see Wright, 328, and al-Muqaddasī, who calls it *tarjahāra*, and describes it as being used for timing irrigation among farmers in the mountains of Daytam at the southwest corner of the Caspian Sea, Goeje, 158. I am grateful to Francis Maddison for the reference from al-Bīrūnī, and to Donald Hill for that from al-Muqaddasī.
63. A number of al-Jazarī's devices (see below), however, such as the elephant clock, employ a sinking bowl in the basic water mechanism.
64. Kurz, 3.

to sink regularly one after the other throughout the twelve double-hours[65]–there are few references to it. Possibly in both regions the rapid development of a more sophisticated water-clock technology meant that this device was ignored and, apart from remote agricultural areas, little used.

In India, however, the device remained in constant use, even at the royal court. A detailed description of it is given in the *Āʾīn-i-Akbarī*[66] (*c.* 1596) and its use throughout northern and southern India,[67] Burma,[68] Ceylon,[69] Siam,[70] and the Malay Archipelago[71] is well attested to by European travellers from the 17th to the 20th centuries. In a somewhat different cultural context, the device was known in medieval Spain,[72] where it was probably used – as it was also in North Africa, the Yemen, and Persia – for timing irrigation.[73] Of all forms of water-clock, except perhaps the outflow clepsydra, it has the longest continuous history.[74]

China

The sinking-bowl water-clock, although known in ancient China, had no history there. The outflow clepsydra, however, known from an early date,[75] was widely used for many centuries even after more sophisticated and accurate timekeepers had been devised. By the former Han period (206 B.C.–A.D. 8), the inflow clepsydra with float and indicator rod had been introduced, and two examples from this period made by Tan Zheng survived until Song times (A.D. 960–1279),

65. Needham & Wang Ling (I), 315. For the Chinese double hours, see Appendix.
66. Gladwin, 3, 12–3.
67. Thurston, 502–6, who notes several sinking-bowl water-clocks in the Madras Museum, and cites a description of them by Picart in *Religious Ceremonies and Customs of the Several Nations of the World* (1731).
68. Nisbet, 288. At each sinking the time was sounded publicly from the *Pahōzin* (bell tower) by the clock-keeper. He, if negligent, could be sold as a slave in the public market and would have to ransom himself.
69. See an example in the Horniman Museum, Forest Hill, London.
70. Ovington, 281; Turpin, i, 142–3. English translation in Pinkerton, ix, 600.
71. Wallace, ii, 169–70. '. . . a watch of two or three on the poop look after the trimming of the sails and call out the hours by the water-clock. This is a very ingenious contrivance, which measures time well in both rough weather and fine. It is simply a bucket half-filled with water, in which floats the half of a well-scraped cocoanut shell. In the bottom of this shell is a very small hole, so that when placed to float in the bucket, a fine thread of water squirts up into it. This gradually fills the shell, and the size of the hole is so adjusted to the capacity of the vessel that, exactly at the end of an hour, plump it goes to the bottom. The watch then cries out the number of hours from sunrise, and sets the shell afloat again empty. This is very good measurer of time. I tested it with my watch and found that it hardly varied a minute from one hour to another, nor did the motion of the vessel have any effect upon it, as the water in the bucket of course kept level. It has a great advantage. For a rude people in being easily understood, in being rather bulky and easy to see, and in the final submergence being accompanied with a little bubbling and commotion of the water, which calls the attention to it. It is also quickily replaced if lost while in harbour.'
72. It is mentioned as a timing device, albeit an unusual one for surveying, in the 10th/11th century, Ms Ripoll 225. See Kurz, 4, n. 7.
73. Glick, 425–6 and references there cited. A modern example (1924) of the instrument from Algeria may be seen in The Science Museum, London. See Ward, no. 8, 9. The clock was lent by the noted ethnographer M.W. Hilton-Simpson.
74. In addition to the sources already mentioned, see the earliest modern account of the instrument by Gilchrist, several details in Gunther, 227–8, and for a recent general survey, Kurz, 3–5.
75. Above, n. 11.

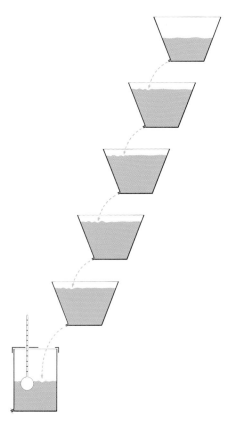

figure 5. Principle of the polyvascular clepsydra.

figure 6. The polyvascular inflow clepsydra at Canton, built in A.D. 1316 by Du Zisheng and Xi Yunxing.

when one of them was drawn and described.[76] Of the origin of the inflow clepsydra in China nothing is known, although the period of its first occurrence corresponds strikingly with that for which we first have information from Greece, i.e. just after Ctesibios. The possibility of contact between the two regions ought not be rejected despite the total absence of evidence. Chinese horologists found two solutions for the problem of pressure compensation in feeding the inflow clepsydra. One was to interpolate one or more intermediary tanks between the reservoir and the float tank, thus reducing the error at each step. As many as six tanks are known to have been used in such 'polyvascular' clepsydrae (figs. 5 & 6).[77] The second method was to insert an overflow tank in the series (fig. 3). This seems to have been done first in the 6th century A.D. Later the two systems were occasionally combined. A further interesting form of clepsydra, which utilized the unequal-arm balance (steelyard), was developed in both large and small forms from the 5th century A.D. onwards.[78]

The technology of the clepsydra was never static in China. From the period of their first appearance, clepsydrae were studied and their behaviour recorded. In the mid-12th century A.D. there were at least fifteen treatises on standard clepsydrae and the accumulating experience of generations meant that development continued and slowly improvements were made. For everyday time-measuring purposes, however, there was no strong need for greater precision, or sophistication in the machine, and within this tradition alone we may reasonably doubt that any dramatic developments would have occurred. However there were other stimuli. At the royal courts, and in particular among the scholars charged with astronomical observations and the rectification of the calendar, there was great interest in automata and an urgent need for labour-saving, self-acting, astronomical demonstrational models.

Control of the calendar was a fundamental symbol of imperial authority. Its accuracy and regularity were considered vital to the harmonious operating of rural Chinese society. Thus a vigilant watch was kept to ensure that the predictions of the official calendar and the observed behaviour of the sun, moon, and stars remained consistent with each other. To do this, accurate demonstrational models embodying the predictions of the calendar were found a useful aid; efforts were made to mechanize them so that they would turn with the same regularity as the heavens of which they were, or were supposed to be, a mirror image. At the same time, such models could serve another purpose. Furnished with automata figures, with gongs or

76. By Xue Shangong (11th century) and by Ludalin (A.D. 1092). See Needham & Wang Ling (I), 321 for reproduction of the diagram and references in n. b.
77. For a surviving medieval example, see Needham & Wang Ling (I), pl. xlv, fig. 141, a photograph of 1912 showing the instrument at Canton made in A.D. 1316 by Du Zisheng and Xi Yunxing. It was used continuously until the early 20th century. For a different view of it *in situ*, see the frontispiece engraving after a photograph by Poyet in Planchon.
78. Needham & Wang Ling (I), 315–9 for all these types and classification. For the steelyard clepsydra (I), 326–8 and Combridge (VI), *passim*.

with bells, they could provide a visual and aural indication of the time, while the celestial globe provided at the same time a convenient picture of the heavens. For astrological purposes, especially for noting the times of cohabitation between the Emperor and various members of his harem, a record of which was essential if the horoscopes of children subsequently born was to be known with accuracy, such a machine was invaluable. Thus in two regards, one relating to the Emperor's outward authority, the other to the internal regulation of his household and ultimately to the imperial succession, there was good reason for interest in the development of a highly accurate, automatic, timekeeping celestial model. It was the continuing effort of Chinese mechanicians to produce such a machine that stimulated a flowering of mechanical and hydraulic ingenuity unrivalled in the world at its time, and fully comparable with the earlier achievements of Alexandria and the later successes of Islam and Europe.[79]

The history of Chinese efforts to produce accurate water-driven mechanical models begins, as far as is known, in the 1st century A.D. Since the story is best read in the words of those who unravelled it in modern times,[80] only a summary will be presented here.

In the 1st century A.D., Chang Heng (78–139), having constructed an armillary sphere, made it turn automatically with clepsydra water. From the same period two archaeological fragments survive – a gear mould, and a gear excavated in 1954 in Shansi Province.[81] Chang Heng's instruments outlasted several dynasties and were available for study by such later constructors as Lu Ji (*fl.* A.D. 220–245), Wang Fan (A.D. 219–257), and Qian Lezhi, who in A.D. 346 was ordered to make a new clepsydra-driven armillary sphere. From the 5th to the 8th centuries several such devices seem to have been built, of which we may mention here that built by Geng Xun (*c.* A.D. 610/20), who is also known to have carried out important work in the development of the public steelyard clepsydra.[82] How these early devices were powered is not at all clear from the surviving evidence, but Needham speculates that 'the mechanism consisted of a vertical waterwheel with cups like a noria. . . . The waterwheel could be attached to a shaft with one trip-lug. . . . Clepsydra drip into the cups would accumulate periodically the torque necessary to turn the lug against the resistance of a leaf-tooth wheel, either itself forming the equatorial ring, or attached to a shaft on the polar axis.'[83]

With Yi Xing and Liang Lingzan (A.D. 723) we reach a landmark in Chinese horology; their machine was more than an astronomical

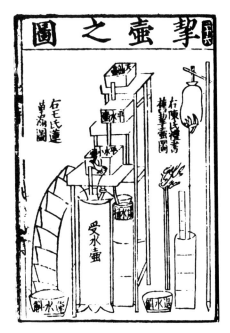

figure 7. The oldest printed picture of a clepsydra. From a Sung edition of Yang Chia's *Liu Ching Thu* (*c.* A.D. 1155). On the left is a combined polyvascular and overflow clepsydra. On the right, the simplest form of inflow device. From Needham & Wang Ling (I), pl. xlvii.

79. For all this, see Needham & Wang Ling (II), 479–92.
80. Needham, Wang Ling & Price, *passim.* Chou, *passim.* See also Needham & Wang Ling (II), 435–546.
81. Chou, 356.
82. Needham & Wang Ling (II), 480.
83. *Ibid,* 481. We may note here the possible survival of one early device into the 20th century in a monastery, probably that of Zhong Zhuwan si near Fuzhou, in the province of Fujian. The clock was seen by Surgeon Captain D.H.C. Given in 1911. No more is known about the device except that it seems to have employed a chain of buckets. See Combridge (II).

model turned and controlled by a clepsydra. Not only were a celestial globe and an armillary sphere turned, but models of the sun and moon were independently geared (as in an orrery) to give them their proper motions. The globe was half-sunk into a wooden casing, the top of which acted as a horizon, thus permitting the times of dawn and dusk, and new and full moon to be determined. Two wooden jacks stood on this horizon striking the hours and quarters on a bell and drum respectively. In addition to all this, the clock had a true escapement (see Glossary) regulating its motion. This device, of which hardly any details are given, seems to have been similar to that employed in the astronomical clocktowers of Zhang Sixun (A.D. 976–79), Zhou Reyan (A.D. 1078–85), and by Su Song (A.D. 1086–89), for which more detailed descriptions survive (catalogue no. 5 & figs. 30–34).[84]

In *c.* 1075 Shen Gua (*c.* A.D. 1031–95) redesigned the overflow clepsydra and recommended changes in the system of calibrated float rods.[85] Thereafter there is less information. In A.D. 1124 Wang Fu began to build an even more complicated device than that of Su Song, since it showed the phases of the moon automatically. His work was interrupted by the attacks of the Jin Tartars on the north Song kingdom, who carried off all that remained of Su Song's clock together with as many mechanicians as they could find. For a while this caused some disruption in the south Song where knowledge of Su Song's device was temporarily lost, but with the recovery of the full description and its publication in 1172, development continued once more, but now as much in the northern Mongol state as in the south. In *c.* A.D. 1276, Guo Shoujing included among the thirteen instruments he made for his reform of the calendar a complicated water-clock with highly elaborate jack-work and very few astronomical indications. He also made a more traditional instrument, a bronze celestial globe for Peking Observatory. This device survived three centuries to be described in 1600 by Matteo Ricci (1552–1610), one of the earliest Jesuit missionaries.[86] There was, however, little else for Ricci to see, for in the revulsion of the Ming revolutionaries against the extravagant waste of the Mongol court, many of the elaborate clepsydrae were destroyed. The last Yuan (Mongol) emperor Shun Di (1333–1368) was himself a clockmaker, building an elaborate automata clock 6–7 feet high. His rebel successors, however, would have nothing to do with such matters:

> When the Emperor T'ai Tsu [Taizu] of the Ming dynasty overthrew the Yuan dynasty, the officer in charge of astronomy of the late dynasty offered him a clepsydra, certain parts of which were made of rock crystal. In it there were two wooden figures which were able to beat the gong and the drum respectively at the right time. But the Emperor T'ai Tsu [Taizu] thought it useless and ordered it to be destroyed.[87]

84. For details of these towers and the complexity of the literary tradition, see Combridge (III).
85. N. Sivin in *D.S.B.*, xii, 376-7.
86. Needham & Wang Ling (I), 368.
87. Quoted from Chou, 337, *cf.* Needham & Wang Ling (II), 510.

The Later Roman Empire

If the achievement of Chinese hydraulic horology is the most dramatic and original to be found in the medieval world, it was not without parallel. From Hellenistic Alexandria, knowledge was transmitted to three regions: to Byzantium, to Persia, Syria, and later Islam, i.e. central Asia, and to Europe. All three regions developed their own characteristic horology. The two chief centres of learning in the Hellenistic world at the beginning of the 5th century A.D. were Alexandria and Athens. At Alexandria, as we have seen, a strong tradition of investigation in theoretical and practical mechanics stemmed from Archimedes and Hero, while even at the more speculative Neoplatonic academy of Athens it was not totally ignored. Proclus (A.D. 4th century), director of the Academy until his death, described in his *Hypotyposis* the method of measuring the apparent diameter of the sun by means of a water-clock.[88] We may assume both the inflow and the outflow forms of the instrument to have been well-known by this time. In A.D. 425 a third centre of learning was established with the revival by Theodosius II (A.D. 401–450) of the school originally founded at Byzantium by Constantine. The three schools had close links and in the following centuries, partly as a result of the labours of John Philoponos (6th century) and those he inspired, a considerable quantity of Greek mathematical and scientific knowledge was assembled and recopied at Byzantium.[89] This was a matter of the greatest importance, for during the 5th and 6th centuries knowledge of Greek had disappeared from Western Europe and North Africa.[90] Among the works preserved at Byzantium were several of Archimedes' mathematical treatises, and some of Hero's, including some now lost.[91] Although there is little direct evidence to support the assertion, it seems certain that a good deal of empirical skill and practical knowledge of construction was also passed on. With it we may assume passed some knowledge and skill in the making of water-clocks. Apart from one reference during the reign of Justinian I,[92] there is little evidence to support this assumption before

88. The method is mentioned by Pappus and other authors (Neugebauer (II), 658, no. 7). A similar method is mentioned critically by Ptolemy, from whose figures Fotheringham calculated that the clocks had a probable error of 12 minutes per hour. This would mean that an actual error of up to 24 minutes in any one hour might be experienced. Neugebauer (II), 657–8 dismisses the matter as 'an obviously fictitious story,' 'only a literary cliché.' While it was perhaps unlikely that many water-clocks of the period could attain the accuracy required by the figures given by Ptolemy (but see the results produced by von Mackensen above, n. 9), the existence of such stories suggests that efforts had been made to use the water-clock in this way, and at the very least attest the familiarity of the instrument.
89. K. Vogel, 'Byzantine Science,' in Hussey, on which much of this section depends.
90. Knowledge of Greek disappeared from northwest Europe during the 5th century A.D. In Italy, Boethius (d.525) and Cassiodorus (d. *c.* 570) were perhaps the last competent Greek scholars, and even in Rome by *c.* 600 the Greek fathers were no longer read in the original. Lemerle, 9.
91. Vogel in Hussey, 266–8.
92. Marquardt, ii, 467, n. 2.

the 9th century, but in a world where all technical knowledge made up one fairly small corpus, it may be inferred. For practical knowledge in general, there is ample evidence. John Philoponos wrote a treatise on the astrolabe; Anthemius of Tralles (d. 534), *mechanikos*, an architect and engineer in the tradition described by Pappus and Vitruvius, wrote a treatise on remarkable engines and began the building of Santa Sophia;[93] and Isidore of Miletus, who succeeded Anthemius in charge of the building of Santa Sophia, wrote a commentary on Hero's now lost treatise ʹχαμαρικα (On the Construction of Vaults), and designed a pair of compasses for drawing parabolas. If in the 6th and 7th centuries there was a decline in the study of the exact sciences at an advanced level, more practical studies were unaffected. As Vogel has pointed out, knowledge of elementary mathematics, of the machines needed for building, and architectural design 'must have been handed down in the guilds of masons, just as merchants and craftsmen must themselves have undertaken the education of the rising generation.'[94] It is significant that many of the fundamental books used were ascribed to Hero.

At some time in the 7th or 8th centuries, Leontius Mechanicus wrote a treatise on how to make a celestial sphere for the latitude of Byzantium.[95] In the reign of Theophilus (d. 842), the father of the patriarch Antony Cassimatas constructed automata that included singing birds and roaring lions to adorn the imperial throne.[96] About the same time (*c.* 840), Leo the Philosopher suggested a method of relaying messages from the frontier to the capital, which depended upon two synchronized water-clocks.[97] Theophilus' automata, and also an elaborate clock, were among items melted down by his successor Michael III in order to pay the army. New automata created for the 'throne of Solomon' of Constantine VII (Porphyrogenitus, 905–959), were seen and wondered at by Liutprand of Cremona during his embassy of 946.[98] This was a period of intensive scientific activity, and although few direct references to water-clocks are known, it is clear that they were in general use in Byzantium, and that the associated Heronic technology of automata, fountains, and other devices had not been lost. To celebrate his victory over the Bulgars in 1014, for example, Basil II redecorated the cathedral which occupied the Parthenon at Athens with frescoes and presented rich gifts to the cathedral treasury. Among them were a golden dove that flapped its wings with a perpetual motion, and a perpetual self-feeding lamp.[99]

93. For a detailed study, see Huxley. For the word μηχανικός, see Downey (I).
94. *Op cit.,* 268. See also Downey (II), esp. 112–4.
95. Περὶ κατασκενῆς Ἀρατειας Σφαιρᾶς. The Greek text was printed in 1536 and 1559 with a Latin translation in *Astronomica Veterum Scripta isagogica Graeca et Latina,* 1589. The only translation into a modern European language is by Halma, 65–73.
96. Brett.
97. Lemerle, 155.
98. Liutprand's description is included in a list of several similar devices, and translated in Rockhill, 207.
99. Miller, 16.

By the mid-12th century, there is some evidence of the transmission of Greek scientific texts from Byzantium to Norman Sicily, where Aristippus (d. 1162) is known to have had a copy of Hero's *Pneumatica* before 1156.[100] From about the same time there is evidence of Byzantine influence on the transmitted Arabic text of a work on the construction of water-clocks traditionally ascribed to Archimedes. In three of the seven known Arabic manuscripts of this work, a section is included by 'Apollonius, the carpenter, the geometrician' describing a musical automaton. From his style Apollonius has been identified as a Byzantine.[101] It may also be significant that in one of the stories of the *Thousand and One Nights*, of which the earliest manuscripts date from the 13th century, an Arab prince encounters speaking statues worked pneumatically when he enters a castle inhabited by a Byzantine princess.[102] Although no objects have survived, it seems probable that water-clocks—whether simple outflow devices used for timing horse races or complex inflow clepsydrae driving automata—were known, understood, and manufactured in the Byzantine Empire.

Islam

The rise of Islam in the early 7th century A.D. and its rapid spread by conquest and persuasion created an empire which stretched from Afghanistan, Persia, and Uzbekistan in the east through the Arabian peninsula, Iraq, Syria, and Anatolia, Egypt, and the North African coast, to Spain and Sicily in the west.[103] This large empire was not simply a political conglomeration. Political expansion also involved, though in complex ways, religious expansion, and the spread of the Islamic religion entailed the spread of the Arabic language, in which the sacred book the *Qur'ān* was written. The area of Islamic conquest, therefore, had a linguistic and, in consequence, a cultural unity similar to that of the Hellenistic world, but in many ways stronger. The Arab conquerors of the most civilized parts of the world were anxious to preserve and acquire the cultural inheritance of the lands they had overrun. The learning of Greece, of Persia, and of Syria was accumulated, absorbed, and developed in Arabic dress. Contacts with Byzantium and with India were also exploited for the knowledge they could bring.

100. Vogel, in Hussey, 281. Haskins, 181–3.
101. Hill (II), 8. Wiedemann & Hauser thought that the whole work was a translation from a Byzantine original possibly via Persia. Drachmann (II), 38, thought it a Muslim work drawing heavily on Philo and Hero. Hill suggests a more convincing composite origin in which he ascribes the basic water machinery to Archimedes, the central sections to a Byzantine (probably) or Persian craftsman, and the last two parts to an Arab. See also de Vaux, *passim*.
102. Khawan, 1086 and n. 14.
103. The new era of Muḥammad was dignified with a new calendar introduced in A.D. 639. This Islamic era counted from the day that the prophet Muḥammad left Mecca 16 July A.D. 622 for Medina. This move is known as the *Hijra* (migration). All dates in the following section are given in both the Islamic and Christian counts. The Islamic date is placed first, indicated by the letters A.H. and is followed by the Christian era date indicated by the letters A.D. Conversions are based upon the tables of Freeman-Grenville.

Philosophy, science, and technology were among the areas of inherited knowledge most eagerly studied in Islam. Knowledge of mechanical timekeeping, of automata, and of mechanical toys was inevitably acquired with it. Probably this occurred at two levels. Firstly, the existing technical skills of craftsmen in Syria and Persia were inherited by their Arab conquerors and developed. Secondly, there was a transmission of literary texts primarily from Greek, although not always directly, which preserved much of the Hellenistic engineering tradition of Alexandria. Of the first of these transmissions it is difficult to say anything with precision, but it seems clear that in both Persia[104] and in the region of Syria an instrument-making technology existed at the time of the Arab conquests. At Jerusalem in the late 5th or 6th century, one of the gifts given to the pilgrims David, Teilavus, and Paternus was a self-sounding bell,[105] while the late-4th-century clock at Gaza described by Procopius presumably survived and was attended for some years. In Syria, the pagan Ṣābian city of Ḥarrān (Carrhae) was a noted centre of metalworking where balances and astrolabes are known to have been made, and whence some technical skills were probably diffused. The second, literary, tradition has also a relation with Ḥarrān, whence came the great translator Thābit b. Qurrà (d. A.H. 288 [A.D. 900–1]) (patronized by Muḥammad b. Mūsà [d. A.H. 259 (A.D. 872–3)]).[106] By his time, however, knowledge of hydraulic technology was already well established in Islam. In his *Kitāb al-Ḥayawān*, Jāḥiẓ (d. A.H. 255 [A.D. 868/9]) mentioned that water-clocks were used by monarchs and scholars to find the hour at night.[107] The earliest treatise known in Arabic that specifically concerns water-clocks is the *Kitāb Arshimīdas fī 'Amal al-binkamāt* (The Book of Archimedes on the Construction of Water-Clocks), which is mentioned in the *Fihrist* of Ibn an-Nadīm (d. *c.* A.H. 380 [A.D. 990/1]). The date of the work, however, is unknown, and the text as it has come down to us appears to be an amalgamation of Greek, Persian, Arabic, and Byzantine elements. Its most recent editor,[108] concluded that while parts of the work describing the basic water machinery and the ball-release mechanism may indeed go back to Archimedes, at least one section cannot be earlier than the mid-12th century. The date of composition of the book as we have it is therefore conjectural, but it seems that at least the first four of the nine sections into which it is divided may have appeared at an early date. Certainly by the 9th century com-

104. See above pp. 8–9. Similar views of the importance of elements deriving from Sasanid Persia are expressed by Hill (V), 20–1, and Khawan, 1086–7.
105. '. . . cimbalum, magis famosum quam pulchrum; quia dulci sono videtur excellare omne oranum. Perjuros damnat, informos curat, et quod magis videtur mirabile, singulis horis, nullo movente, sonabat.' Roberts, Appendix vi, 308a citing from the *Book of Llandaff*. The passage is also excerpted in Wood, 14–5.
106. For metalworking and astrolabe-making at Ḥarrān, see Maddison & Turner, 86–7. A revised version of part of the work will appear as an introduction to Brieux & Maddison. For brief comments, see Turner (III). For the religion of the Sabians, see Dodge. For Muḥammad b. Mūsà, see below and Hill (V), 3–6.
107. Siddiqi, 246.
108. Hill (II), 9. The work is also discussed in Hill (VI), ch. II.

plicated hydraulic automata clocks were being made, for in A.D. 807 a clock with falling brass balls and horsemen who came out of doors at each hour[109] was presented by vassals of Harūn ar-Rashīd to Charlemagne.

In the course of the 9th century, Hero's *Mechanics* was translated by Qustà b. Luqā, and although we cannot be precise about details, it seems clear that by the end of this century a good deal of Hellenistic automata technology had been absorbed in Islam and was already being developed. The outstanding achievement of the period was probably the *Kitāb al-Ḥiyal* (Book of Ingenious Devices) of the Banū Mūsà b. Shākir, which exemplifies Islamic pneumatic technology in its collection of lamps (self-trimming and appearing to be perpetual), water- or wine-dispensing vessels, whistles, pipettes, and fountains. This, as Hill has indicated, shows close overlap in twenty-five of the devices described with Greek antecedents[110] but elsewhere it goes far beyond the work of Philo and Hero. Indeed, within the limits of medieval technology, the Banū Mūsà treatise virtually exhausted the subject.

The treatise of the Banū Mūsà included no clocks,[111] but they are briefly mentioned in the description of the works of *ḥiyal* (ingenious devices) included by Abu 'Abdallah al-Khwārizmī in his scientific encyclopedia *Mafātiḥ al-'Ulūm* (The Keys of the Sciences).[112] The technology of water-clocks, however, is closely associated with that of fountains, automata, and other such gadgets, and it would be unreasonable to assume that there was no activity in this field. Even so, in the two centuries between the gift to Charlemagne and Ibn az-Zarqellu (Latin: Azarchiel) in the mid-5th/11th century there is a dearth of evidence apart from the undatable Archimedes treatise, several references to water-clocks, both inflow and outflow, in the works of al-Bīrūnī (unfortunately without details), and a vague reference that associates a clock with the great physicist Ibn al-Haytham (A.H. *c.* 354–430 [A.D. 965–1038/9]).[113] In 1085, however, at the fall of Toledo to Alphonso VI of Leon and Castile, the Christian conquerors encountered two water-clocks which had been erected on the banks of the Tagus by Ibn az-Zarqellu (d. 8 Dhū-l hijja 493 = 15 October A.D. 1100). These were regulated to show the phase of the moon, and were apparently of some considerable size. Perhaps some knowledge was gained from them for at least one of

109. Eginhard, *Annales Francorum; Chronicon Turonense*. The relevant passages are quoted and translated in Beckmann, i, 343.
110. Hill (V), 21.
111. They do, however, remark of a lamp described in their treatise 'from which the wick emerges of its own accord' that 'it is possible with these arrangements to make a lamp that shows the [passage of the] hours, and whenever an hour elapses a ball drops.' *Ibid.*, 237.
112. Al-Khwārizmī, 235. I wish to thank G. Saliba for this reference.
113. 'People have made them [sand- and water-clocks] in many forms, but they produce the hours and the large divisions of the hours, and not all of them produce the single hours which are equivalent to the divisions of the celestial sphere, except the clock [*Binkām*] that was mentioned by Ibn al-Haytham al-Misrī based upon [the use] of water.' Al-Khāzinī, *Kitāb Mīzān al-Hikma* (Book of the Balance of Wisdom) pt. viii, cited from Hill (VI). For references in al-Bīrūnī's *Ifrād al-maqāl fī amr az-Zilāl*, see Kennedy, i, 229, *cf.* i, 12 & 150.

them continued to work until 1133.[114] But, that much may remain to be discovered in the field of Islamic technology and horology is illustrated by the recent recovery of a copy (mutilated) of a hitherto unknown treatise on clocks and automata from Islamic Spain. This, the *Kitāb al-asrār fī nātā' ij al-afkār* (The Book of Secrets about the Results of Thoughts), has been attributed to Muḥammad or Aḥmad b. Khalaf al-Murādī,[115] about whom nothing is known except that he probably lived in the late-5th/11th century.

Although clearly in the same tradition as the Archimedes treatise, the Banū Mūsà, and later al-Jazarī, the treatise of al-Murādī displays many differences. There are seventeen clocks showing unequal hours and five automata among the thirty-one devices described by al-Murādī. All his machines are large, robust, and powerful. Here are no delicate, sophisticated toys to grace the tables of princes and noble lords, such as occur in the pages of the Banū Mūsà and al-Jazarī. Al-Murādī's machines are often powered by a vertical water-wheel[116] and make much use of complex gearing. Indeed it is in this respect that the treatise is perhaps most remarkable. For in addition to all the usual forms of gears — parallel-meshing, right-angle-meshing, and worm-and-pinion — al-Murādī certainly employed segmental gears, and possibly epicycloidal ones as well. A local peculiarity of his designs was the use of mercury inside tilting balance-arms, and to some extent the work displays signs of being backward. Thus the basic water machinery of the clocks is a crude outflow clepsydra of constant cross-section and siphon outlet and although the author knew the ball-release mechanism described in the Archimedes treatise,[117] he did not use the outflow control system there described. Communication between eastern Islam and Andalusia was no doubt slow, but al-Murādī also comments that engineering had fallen into disuse.

In A.H. 515 (A.D. 1121/2), Abu'l Fatḥ 'Abd ar-Raḥmān al Manṣūr al-Khāzinī, by origin a Greek slave, completed his treatise *Kitāb Mīzān al-Ḥikma* (The Book of the Balance of Wisdom). This is an excellent survey of contemporary mechanisms and hydrostatics, distinguished by the author's remarkably objective and accurate approach to observation and experiment.[118] In the eighth book of the treatise, al-Khāzinī describes in some detail the construction and use of two forms of steelyard clepsydra which might be operated with water or with sand. The steelyard clepsydra had, of course, a long history in China;[119] it was known in the Byzantine empire; and it

---

114. Millas, 6–9.
115. Attention was drawn to the treatise in 1975 by David A. King. Its engineering content and place in the history of Islamic technology have subsequently been discussed by Hill (III), and Hill (IV), ch. 3. Villuendas, *passim*. See also Sabra.
116. *Cf.* the comments on this similarity with Chinese clocks, in Hill (III), 38–9.
117. Hill (II), 19–20; Hill (III), 40–2.
118. The book has been discussed with translated extracts and annotations by Khanikoff.
119. Needham & Wang Ling (II), sec. 26c. Combridge (VI), who re-translates a 10th- or 11th-century description of the device, considers its origin to be Islamic. Lorch, however, argues for an Hellenistic origin.

was adapted to sound an alarm at a predetermined time, as is described in Hebrew in the *Zohar*.[120] Certainly the device seems to have been simple to operate and relatively efficient.[121] The permanent attendance of a clock-keeper was required to mark up the hours, but since virtually all medieval clocks required full-time clock-keepers this is no denigration of the machine.

From the early years of the late-6th/12th and early-7th/13th century, we have a considerable quantity of evidence surviving for the scale and activities of Islamic technicians and horologists. In A.H. 600 (A.D. 1203/4) Ridwān b. Muḥammad b. 'Alī b. Rustam al-Khurāsānī as-Sā'ātī wrote a description of the great clock that his father Muhammad b. 'Ali b. Rustam al-Khurāsānī as-Sā'ātī (d. A.H. 569 [A.D. 1173/4]) had built at the Jayrūn gate to the east of the great Ummayad Mosque in Damascus. The clock, which survived at least until the mid-8th/14th century, was also described several times by travellers—the most complete description being given by Ibn Jubayr in A.H. 580 (A.D. 1184/5). Like other monumental clocks of its kind, the Damascus example had brass falcons which dropped balls onto gongs to sound the hour, doors which opened to indicate the hour, and a semicircle of glass roundels in an arch above, one of which lit up at each hour of the night. Ridwān in his treatise describes the clock in some detail and claims several innovations for his father. These included the use of a fully circular flow-regulator, a gearing system which reduced the distance the float had to travel, and the semicircle for the night, plus some other minor embellishments of his own invention. The clock, which was complicated, broke down frequently, partly because of flexure in its support structure. Ridwān himself looked after the clock for many years, and it is an interesting reflection on the nature of Islamic horology that he is scathing in his comments on the attempts of other craftsmen to maintain it. Even when allowance is made for Ridwān's proper family pride, his comments suggest that between the level of ability displayed by the treatises, and the capabilities of everyday workmen, there may have been considerable difference.[122]

In A.H. 602 (A.D. 1205/6) the engineer to the Artuqid court at Diyār Bakr, Ibn ar-Razzāz al-Jazarī, completed a treatise which he had been requested to write by his master, Nāsir ad-Dīn. This, the *Kitāb fī ma'rifat al-ḥiyal al-handisiya* (The Book of Knowledge of Ingenious Mechanical Devices), was a description of the devices he had invented and made in the previous twenty-five years. It is the peak of medieval Islamic technology.[123] Included in the work are six

---

120. Thirteenth century, probably written in Spain, perhaps by Moses of Leon (d. 1305). The passage is quoted, and discussed, in Kurz, 16–8.
121. In a modern half-scale working model, time 'was indicated accurately within about ±1½%,' Combridge (VI), 532.
122. This account is based entirely on Hill (VI), ch. 5, which offers a full reconstruction of the clock. *Cf.* Siddiqi, 247–8.
123. Hill (I). The clocks are also discussed in Hill (VI), ch. 6.

figure 8. The castle water-clock of
Ibn ar-Razzāz al-Jazarī (A.D. 1206).
Library of the Topkapı Sarayı Müzesı,
Istanbul, Ms 3472.

water-clocks, which although large and complex are totally practical.[124] They are also consciously traditional although embodying
innovations. Al-Jazarī was aware of his place in a long tradition. He
acknowledges his predecessors, and castigates their blunders. His
book not only describes the devices he has made but also gives complete directions for their construction. The first clock described, the
castle water-clock (fig. 8), is not very dissimilar from that of Ridwān, and may be considered as the typical form of the public clock.
The others are more unusual, the fifth being a portable outflow clepsydra. All are decorative.

From the number of manuscripts that have survived, many beautifully illustrated,[125] and ranging in date over six centuries, it is clear
that al-Jazarī's work was much esteemed both in his lifetime and
after. This in itself is some evidence of continuing interest in water-
clocks in the later Middle Ages. For once the impression can be

124. A reconstruction of one of the clocks was built for the exhibition 'Science and Technology
in Islam,' at The Science Museum, London, in 1976, following al-Jazarī's instructions and
methods.
125. There is an extensive literature on the miniatures illustrating the treatise. See Stchoukine,
Coomaraswamy, with extensive bibliography, and Hill (IV).

substantiated. In A.H. 633 (A.D. 1235/6) a monumental water-clock that announced the appointed hours of prayer and the time both by day and by night was completed in the entrance hall to the Mustanṣirīya college.[126] Since the college was intended to be the most magnificent in the empire, no pains were spared on the clock, and from the description given by Ibn al-Furāt[127] it seems indeed to have been remarkably similar to the castle clock of al-Jazarī. The clock was built by 'Alī b. Taghleb b. Abī ad-Ḍiyā as-Sā'ātī (A.H. 601–683 [A.D. 1204/5–1284/5]) and survived to be wondered at for some years. Some decades later there is a record of the construction of a clock in the Qarawiyyin mosque in Fez, Morocco by Abu 'Abd Allah Muḥammad b. al-Habbāq at-Tilimsānī in A.H. 685 (A.D. 1286/7). A second clock was constructed in the same mosque early in the following century by Abu 'Abd Allah Muḥammad as-Sinhāgī and this in turn was reconstructed in A.H. 763 (A.D. 1361/2) by Abu 'Abd Allah Muḥammad al-'Arabī. Parts of this clock, including a large rotating astrolabic dial survive *in situ*,[128] as do the façade, gongs, windows, and ball-channels of another clock at Fez on the Bū'anāniyya mosque (fig. 9). In A.H. 14 Jumādà I, 758 (A.D. 6 May

figure 9. The gongs and ball-channels of the Fez water-clock. Postcard of *c.* 1920. (Photograph: Alain Brieux)

126. Le Strange, 267.
127. His description, with some other accounts, is translated in Jawad, 31–4.
128. Price (I). There is a photograph of the astrolabe dial by Wim Swaam in Landau, 119. For the astrolabe in general, see Vol. I part 1 of this catalogue.

1357) this clock was finished by Abu-l-Ḥasan ʿAlī b. Aḥmad at-Til-imsānī,[129] who was also responsible for a clepsydra with automata kept in the royal palace of Abū Ḥammū II (A.H. 760–791 [A.D. 1358/9–1388/9]) at Tlemcen. This second clock was displayed for the first time in A.H. 770 (A.D. 1368/9) to increase the magnificence of the king in the eyes of his people at the feast of *Maulad* (the prophet Muḥammad's birthday), one of the few occasions on which the king was publicly seen. Descriptions of the piece are preserved in chronicles and poems written in its praise by Yaḥyā b. Khaldūn (assassinated A.H. 780 [A.D. 1378/9]), the king's secretary. In addition to the row of doors for the hours (those on the ends being larger than the other ten), two eagles to drop balls into brass bowls, and a moon moving through a semicircle to mark the time at night, the clock was adorned with automata figures of a bird and two chicks in a rose bush, underneath which lurked a serpent. At each hour the snake climbed up the bush to attack the chicks, whose parents made defensive noises, while from the hour door a slave girl came forth holding a tablet with verses in one hand and raising the other to her mouth in a salutation. Although little more is known about the device, it seems to have been well-preserved since it is mentioned at the *Maulad* feast as late as A.H. 814 (A.D. 1411/12).[130]

Abu-l-Ḥasan was handsomely rewarded for his work with a pension of one-thousand gold pieces. Probably he made other clocks and it is perhaps not stretching speculation too far to think of him as a later Maghrib equivalent of al-Jazarī. Of other men like him and al Jazarī, whom we may postulate existed in greater and lesser courts and palaces throughout Islam, nothing at all is known, but we may hazard one generalization: such men were few in number and dependent for their existence almost exclusively upon the patronage of wealthy rulers. The sophisticated tradition of automata clocks belongs in the courts and in the towns. It accompanies the life of leisure, prestige, and wealth. Public clocks were constructed to adorn the buildings erected by the mighty. They underlined position and power. They were expensive and, in consequence, they were perhaps not widely spread.

Apart from the North African water-clocks of Fez and Tlemcen, we know, at present, little more about Islamic horology. Clearly the tradition did not die out immediately, but it certainly weakened. The preoccupation of the Ottoman state with warfare, perhaps meant diminution of patrons for complex pieces, and the 16th century saw a new, and cheaper source of such devices to titillate the fancy of sultans. For the 16th century was characterized by an increasing number of diplomatic missions from European monarchs. Extravagant gifts were an essential part of such missions, and at least from the 1530's onwards such gifts were very often elaborate automaton

129. Price (I); Mayer (I), 40. Good illustrations of the remains may be found in Tardy (I), 69–71; Landau, 91 (by Wim Swaam) and in Nasr, 117 (by Roland Michaud).
130. For this account of Abu-l-Ḥasan at Tlemcen, see Bargès, 368–76.

clocks.[131] They were as we might expect, very well received, being in an ancient tradition, but they were no longer hydraulically driven. For these were the first masterpieces of the European tradition of weight- and spring-driven clocks, and to the ancient appeal of automata, they offered all the attractions of novelty. The change marked the end of the ancient hydraulic tradition.

The Medieval Latin West

The fall of the Roman Empire in the West, despite its catastrophic consequences for Graeco-Roman literary culture, was perhaps not so serious for technology. As noted above, a tradition of fine craftsmanship, and even some of its literary monuments, was transmitted to the Byzantine Empire from Alexandria and Syria and between barbarian Europe and Byzantium there was, even in the 5th and 6th centuries, some contact. In early medieval Europe ingenious time-keeping devices, automata, and other toys seem indeed to have been no more uncommon and certainly no less fascinating than they were in Byzantium or Islam. For the exact nature of these devices, their technical details, how and where they were made, and by whom, we have little precise information, and neither in Byzantium nor in Europe are there any treatises comparable with those of the Banū Mūsà or al-Jazarī in Islam. But of the existence of water-clocks, and of water-alarms there is no possible doubt.

Unlike the more speculative and mathematical branches of science, relatively little of medieval Europe's horological knowledge appears to have been transmitted from Islam. Although from this generalization we must except the Iberian peninsula and Sicily (where a surviving inscription in Greek, Latin, and Arabic records a *horologium* erected by Roger II in 1142[132]), in general we find few indications among the scattered surviving evidence of the characteristic features of the Islamic tradition such as the ball-dropping falcons and eagles, the row of doors which opened to indicate the hour, and the arch of roundels which lit up to show the hour at night. Given the deficient nature of the evidence, this is not to say that there was no influence from Islam, but at present it seems that the tenuous survival in northwest Europe of late-Roman technical skills, perhaps stimulated by occasional contact with Byzantium, led to the development of horological devices suitable for local needs. The most characteristic of these in medieval Europe seems to have been a relatively simple water-driven alarm used by the sacristan or sub-sacristan in monastic houses to remind him of

131. For western diplomatic gifts of clocks and automata, see Kurz, 20-53; Mraz, *passim*. The first western clockmaker in the Ottoman state is said to have been requested by Mehmet II from the Signoria of Venice.
132. Ungerer, 28-9.

grota
uit rex
ezechi
af ufqʒ ad mor
tem. roʒauit ad
dnm. 7 addidit
drīs diebʒ fuis
·xv· annos. 7 de
dit ei fignū per
yfaiam ppham.
ut fol ·x· gradibʒ
retrorfū in orolo
gio reuerteref

Hoc qʒ fol
decem
gradi
bʒ reuerfuʒ e

figure 10. A medieval monastic water-clock. Bodleian Library, Oxford. Ms Bodley 270b. f. 183v.

when to sound the signal for the different offices that punctuated monastic days and nights. A description of such a device is contained in a Spanish manuscript, apparently uninfluenced by its proximity to Islam, which probably dates from the mid-11th century.[133] A century-and-a-half later, a bell-sounding device is the subject of the only known illustration of a medieval water-clock[134] (fig. 10). That such devices were used in European monastic communities in the 11th century is evident from numerous references to 'horologia' in monastic rules of the period,[135] and from several more detailed pieces of evidence in the succeeding centuries.[136] Their use,

133. The text, from Ms Ripoll 225 now in the Archivo de la Corona de Aragón, Barcelona, has been studied and translated by Maddison, Scott, & Kent.
134. Ms Bodley 270b f 183v, a north French moralized bible of the first quarter (c. 1223-6) of the 13th century. For divergent interpretations of the clock's operation, see Drover (I); Drover (II); White (I), 120–1; Combridge (V); Sleeswyck, 63.
135. For a representative selection, see Beckmann, i, 346–9.
136. For a summary of this evidence, see Drover (I). The most important is the set of rules for adjusting a water-clock for the unequal hours described on fragments of slate found at Villers Abbey near Brussels in 1894. These date from 1267 or 1268. See Sheridan, and more recently d'Haenens.

however, extends back at least to the 9th century when Hildemar remarked 'He who wishes to [observe the hours] for the offices properly, must have *horologium aquae*.'[137] Earlier than this they were perhaps infrequent, although Cassiodorus (A.D. 485–*c*. 580) mentions that he had supplied the monks in his foundation at St. Andiol with both a sundial and a water-clock, 'which marks the hours both day and night as frequently upon some days there is no sunshine.'[138]

If the monastic alarm represents the survival in Europe of a relatively primitive strand of Hellenistic technology, it was paralleled by more sophisticated devices. The anaphoric clock, for example, described by Vitruvius but dating back perhaps as far as Ctesibios, may never have completely disappeared from Europe. Fragments of two anaphoric clock dials dating from between the 1st and 3rd centuries A.D. have been found in Europe at Grand (Vosges) and at Salzburg.[139] Thereafter we have a gap of seven centuries until in the 9th century a number of constellation diagrams are found, usually associated with manuscripts of Aratus, which not only show knowledge of the stereographic projection (required for the construction of astrolabes and anaphoric clocks), but also seem to have a relation with the dial arrangements of the anaphoric clock. Since a number of late-medieval clocks, among them that of Richard of Wallingford in the early 14th century, share similar arrangements, it seems possible that a rather weak tradition of anaphoric clocks, or at least of certain of its characteristic features, survived in early medieval Europe.[140]

Alongside the anaphoric clock, other astronomical clocks and water-driven models were known. Here also there was some direct transmission from late antiquity, for in a letter to Boethius (A.D. 507) requesting that he supply a sundial and a water-clock that Gondebaud, King of the Burgundians, had requested, the Emperor Theodoric speaks eloquently of the accomplishments of the mathematical arts but then wonders rhetorically why he discusses trivial things when he discourses on an art which can imitate the heavens themselves ('Parua de illa referimus, cui caelum imitari fas est'). He mentions the sphere of Archimedes and is obviously familiar with astronomical models of late antiquity. How much of this knowledge survived the succeeding centuries is a matter for speculation, although something was transmitted since a sundial

---

137. Cited from Martene, *de Ritibus Ecclesiastica*, iv, 5, by Beckmann, i, 345.
138. *Ibid.* 342. See also Hodgkin.
139. The Salzburg fragment is discussed by Bennendorf, Weiss, & Rehm, 196–7. The second fragment from Grand was found in a well in 1886 with other metal and ceramic fragments. Briefly described by Werly as a calendar device, it formed part of the collection of H. Hoffman. Sold with this collection (Lot 653) at Hôtel Drouot in May 1888, it is now in the Musée Nationale des Antiquités, St. Germain-en-Laye. I am grateful to Mr. & Mrs. R.S. Webster for a copy of the entry in the Hoffman catalogue. For a detailed reconstruction by Francis Maitzner, see Tardy (I), x–xviii.
140. This hypothesis is argued out by North (II). We may add in support of this hypothesis that manuscripts of Vitruvius were not uncommon in European monasteries and could have supplied a stimulus to horologically inclined brothers. For an analogous example of Vitruvian influence which illustrates the dissemination of his treatise in England, see Harrison.

and a water-clock were duly constructed and sent to Gondebaud.[141] Thereafter there is no information until the time of Gerbert (later Pope Sylvester II), who mentions a clepsydra in one of his letters, and is said to have constructed a water-clock at Ravenna *c.* A.D. 998–999.[142] Shortly afterward, the anonymous author of a life of William, Abbot of Hirshau, remarked that 'he devised a clock by nature agreeable to the model of the celestial hemisphere,'[143] which would seem to imply some kind of astronomical clock. By this time, however, there may have been some transmission of knowledge from Islam, probably through Spain. Gerbert is known to have studied in Spain, and the earliest Latin treatises on the astrolabe by Lupitus and Hermann of Reichenau depend on Arabic originals.[144] Moreover, in A.D. 807 a typically Islamic water-clock with automata had been sent as a gift to Charlemagne.[145] Possibly in the 10th and 11th centuries some knowledge of Islamic and Byzantine clocks and automata technology was transmitted to the West, and mingled with local traditions, which, although perhaps less sophisticated, were still competent. In the mid-10th century, Liutprand of Cremona described the automata in the Byzantine throne of Solomon,[146] but we have little other evidence of the transmission of horology and automata during the following century. In 1183 a guild of water-clock makers was established at Cologne[147] and in the following centuries ingenious devices became increasingly familiar to Christian Europe. Several accounts of automata seen in Oriental courts are to be found in the travel narratives of the 12th, 13th, and 14th centuries. More important, as perhaps attesting to a tradition of indigenous products, are the many references to brazen birds who sing, golden trees of which the leaves rustle, serpents who attack chicks, knights on horseback who joust or guard entrances to charmed chambers, and even to whole rooms which revolve and bemuse the beholders in 12th- and 13th-century romances. One product of this tradition, a table fountain which rang bells as jets of water or wine fell onto vertical turbines, has survived. It dates probably from the mid-14th century, and is French.[148] In so far as any in-

---

141. Theodoric's letter was of course written by Cassiodorus. See *Magni Aurelii Cassiodori Senatoris Opera Pars I Variarum libri XII* (ed. A.J. Fridh) in *Corpus Christianorum. Series Latina* XCVI, Turnholt, 1973, 49–51 & 52. Presumably when the clock was sent, it was accompanied by a trained clock-keeper as Gondebard had requested. That the device was in fact a much earlier Roman clock is a theory unsupported by any evidence even by its originator, Forlatti. That the unusual open tower marked *Orfanum* (recte *organum*) on the 9th-century pictorial map of Verona (Bibl. Capitolari, Verona: Cod CXIV) housed a clepsydra is a less implausible suggestion, although since the tower is beside the river it is equally likely that it housed pumping or grinding machinery.

142. Letter No. 161 to Brother Adam, 10 March 989, see Lattin and North (II), 396–7 n. 42. It is interesting to note also that later tradition told stories of Gerbert the thaumaturge in which automata play an important part. See Spargo, 121–2.

143. Beckmann, i, 346. 'Naturale horologium ad exemplum cælestis hæmispherii excogitasse.'

144. See Turner (III).

145. Eginhard, *Annales Francorum*, anno 807.

146. See above, p. 16.

147. White (I), 120.

148. It is now in the Cleveland Museum of Art (Ohio). See Milliken and *Fastes*, 236–8, where it is more fully described and where other fragments are listed. For convenient summaries of automata both in fact and fiction, see Brett, Sherwood, Bruce, and Spargo, ch. IV *passim*.

dication of the mechanisms of these devices is given, the automata of Europe appear to have been somewhat less sophisticated than those of Islam or China, and recourse was occasionally made to concealed human agents when mechanical means did not produce the desired effect.[149] Despite this deficiency, it is clear that automata were becoming well-known and widely manufactured in the 12th and 13th centuries, and that they were also amalgamated into the tradition of clock-making. Public clocks and smaller examples made for the pleasure of princes and their courts seem to have been adorned with automata and the tradition carried over to the new weight-driven devices developed in the late 13th century. It was thus perpetuated in the long tradition of mechanical horology.

The 13th century saw rapid developments in all branches of technology. Horology was no exception, and it is in this context of ferment and investigation that its development should be seen.[150] By 1220 the Cologne guild of water-clock makers had expanded to fill an entire street, the Urlogengasse,[151] and an anonymous, as yet

figure 11. Compartmented cylinder mercury clock driving an astrolabe dial. From the *Libros del Saber de Astronomía* of Alfonso the Wise, *c.* 1276. After Rico y Sinobas.

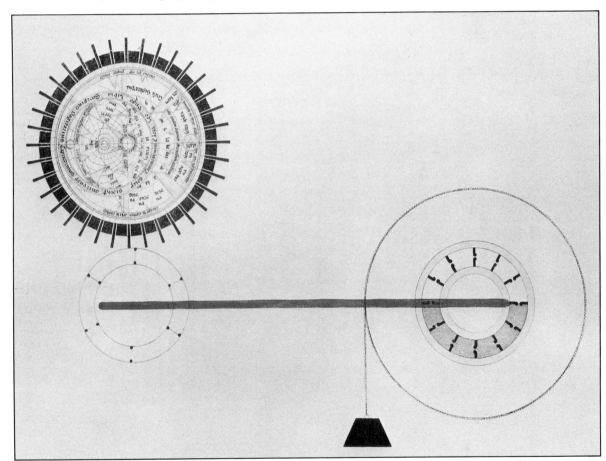

149. For example, the device taken to the court of the Mogul Khan at Caracorum by the son of William, a goldsmith, of Paris. This was a complex simultaneous dispenser of several different kinds of drink. When an angel seated on top of a tree gave a blast on his trumpet, the drinks ran. Although William intended to have effected this trumpet blast with bellows, he was unsuccessful and a man was hidden inside the tree to do it. The device was described by William of Rubruck, but it is significant to find such an item already being exported from Europe to the East. See Rockhill, 107 ff.
150. For the general technological context, see White (I), 79–134; Gille (I), *passim*.
151. White (I), 120.

unpublished treatise describing a simple form of water-clock also survives from early decades of the century.[152] From the middle decades there is an account of a complex geared planetary instrument perhaps intended to be driven by water. In his commentary on the Pseudo-Aristotelian *Problems*, Pietro d'Abano (1257– *c.* 1315) discussed a clepsydra, and simpler water-clocks indicating the hour were used in monasteries throughout Europe. Thus in England one William *aurifaber* held one virgate of land of the abbott of St. Mary's, Glastonbury (1252–61) in exchange for three *solidi* and various services, one of which was repairing of the water-clock (*clipsadra*).[153] In Spain a revival of activity is attested at the Toledo court of Alfonso X 'el Sabio' who commissioned numerous translations of philosophical and scientific texts from Arabic,[154] together with the compilation of an astronomical encyclopedia, the *Libros del Saber*.[155] A section of this work was devoted to horology, describing among other devices an outflow clepsydra,[156] and a mercury-controlled device (fig. 11) of novel form.[157] Here, however, it is interesting to note that the author of this latter section, Ishāq b. Sīd, was also the copyist of the only surviving manuscript of the *Kitāb al-asrār* of al-Murādī.[158] This work, Ishāq says, he found difficult to understand, but he eventually succeeded and made most of the devices that it described. Clearly the Islamic technical tradition at Toledo was more than just a bookish one.

At the same time in the 13th century that these developments took place in traditional hydraulic clock and automata technology, work was proceeding that would ultimately displace the tradition; the last quarter of the 13th century saw efforts made to find methods to control the fall of a heavy weight, and so to drive clocks, automata displays, and astronomical models. The mercury drum of Ishāq b. Sīd in the *Libros del Saber* was one of these efforts and there were many more.[159] Ultimately they led to the discovery of an escapement which did not require the use of a liquid, and that in cold northern climes had obvious advantages. For the ancient hydraulic tradition, however, it was a disaster. The functions of the clepsydra were transferred to the new machines. Planetary models, automata, planispheres, anaphoric and astrolabe dials could all be driven by it. But the water-clock lingered on. Its simpler forms, the sinking-bowl water-clock and the outflow clepsydra were useful in monasteries and agrarian areas. Thus water-clocks (*ollarum horologia*: clocks of earthenware vessels) are mentioned at St. Alban's

152. Codex Vaticanus Latinus 5367. An edition and translation of this text is being prepared by Francis Maddison & Bryan Scott.
153. For the geared planetary instrument, see North (I), 3; for Pietro d'Abano, his *Problemata Aristotelis...antiqua et nova...*, XVI: 7. The *editio princeps* was at Mantua in 1475. For William *aurifaber*, Brockhaus, i, 515, no. 1901.
154. For this highly important translation school, see Proctor.
155. Edited by Rico.
156. *Ibid.*, II, 24–55.
157. *Ibid.*, II, 65–5. See below, p. 37.
158. Villuendas, 395–6.
159. For a survey of these matters, see Price (II).

Abbey during the rule of John de Moyns (1302–1308), and it was surely for a very simple contrivance that 1d. was paid at Southampton in 1399.[160] In about 1418 Giovanni Fontana (mid-1390's–post-1454) found the water-clock sufficiently interesting to write a short treatise on it.[161] Even so, the complex astronomical clepsydra, with or without automata, does seem to have disappeared from 15th-century Europe, and in the succeeding century examples of the new all-mechanical European 'horloge' would also undermine its position in Islam.[162] But, the water-clock had not lost all its usefulness to European society and like the Hellenistic technology which had created it, it was to experience a revival.

Early Modern Europe

The European Renaissance is an astonishing example of applied antiquarianism. For a century or more, the cultured communities of the most advanced nations in Europe devoted themselves to a spurious re-creation of a dead society. The lost civilizations of Greece and Rome became the criteria of all judgements, the models for all conduct, and the mirror in which men wished to see themselves reflected playing the parts of the ancient Greeks and Romans. The desire to re-create the past extended to the minutest details and was, fortunately, a total failure. Nonetheless it stimulated scholarly activity in the recovery of ancient texts and, although primarily a literary and educational movement, it also affected science and technology. In the history of the water-clock and its associated technology this was particularly important, for the backward-looking habit of European society aided the revival of a moribund instrument.[163]

The revival of the water-clock in the Renaissance is a subject as yet inadequately known. To investigate the subject in detail is a task which cannot be undertaken here. It is clear, however, that as in late antiquity, as in Byzantium, and as in Islam, the works of Hero were of importance. Although some of Hero's treatises were known in the Middle Ages, only one Greek manuscript, of the late 15th century, is known to survive. From the 16th century, however, nearly

---

160. *Gesta Abbatum monasterii S. Albani* 1302–1308, cited from Brockhaus, iii, 94, no. 5490; for Southampton, Rogers, i, 647. A later water-clock treatise of 1341 is discussed below, p. 37.
161. This was perhaps intended to be one of a group of treatises on different kinds of clocks. See Clagett 10–13, 25, and more briefly Thorndike, iv, 156–7.
162. Kurz, *passim*. The parts of the ancient hydraulic technology not employing a time-measuring element were unaffected by development of weight- and spring-driven timekeepers, and presumably a tradition of trick drinking vessels, fountains and hydraulic automata continued and ultimately linked up with the Renaissance revival of these subjects. In 1338 the two traditions still coexisted when six Venetian merchants took to the Sultan of Delhi a clock (rellogio) and an automatic fountain (Lopez 488, n. 16). Note that the Cleveland 14th-century table fountain (n. 148) was discovered buried in the gardens of a palace at Constantinople (Milliken, 37).
163. A comparable example of the effort to re-create the technical details of a classical activity is provided by the development of stage machinery and scenic effect. See Campbell, and Yates (who discusses more generally the revival of the arts of the μηχανοι – the Heronic tradition of Pappus – which she calls the 'Vitruvian tradition').

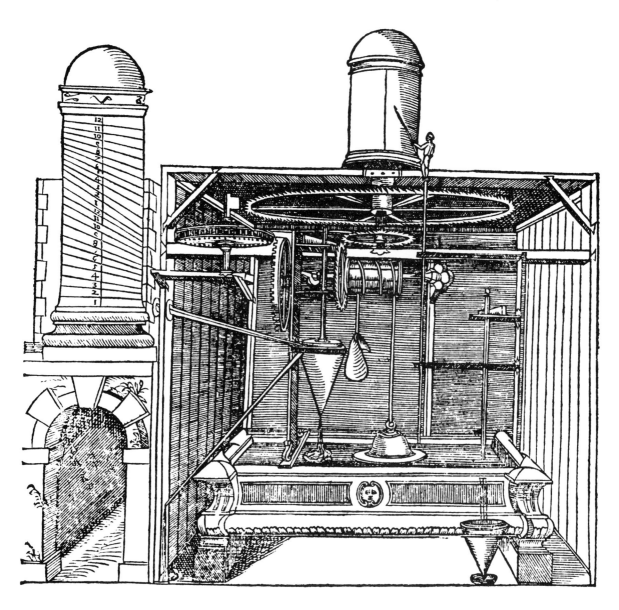

figure 12. A Renaissance conception of Vitruvius' 'parastatic' clock. From Daniele Barbaro's edition of Vitruvius, *De Architectura . . .*, 1567, 324.

one-hundred copies are extant. In 1474, Regiomontanus included Hero's works in the list of Greek mathematical works that he intended to translate and publish.[164] In 1501 a paraphrase of Hero's work on siphons was included in Giorgio Valla's *de Expectendis et fugiendis rebus.* Although there are several references to him thereafter, it was not until 1575 that a full Latin translation was produced by Federico Commandino.[165] Reprinted in 1585 and 1680, it was to remain the standard edition until the 19th century. After 1575 there were several other editions. An Italian translation of Commandino[166] appeared in 1589 and was twice reprinted, followed in 1592 by a learned edition by Alessandro Giorgio which discussed the mechanisms of the devices.[167] About a century later, in 1687, a Ger-

164. For all this, see Boas, and references there given.
165. *Heronis Alexandrini Spiritalium Liber,* 1575.
166. Battista Aleotti, *Gli Artifitiosi, et curiosi moti Spiritali di Herrone,* 1589.
167. *Spiritale di Herone Alessandrino,* Urbino, 1592, Venice, 1595.

man edition, twice reprinted, appeared, and in the same year the Greek text was printed for the first time.[168]

The influence of Hero on writers on mechanisms, hydraulics, and pneumatics was considerable. To list the names of Girolamo Cardano, Jacques Besson, Giovanni Battista della Porta, Cornelius Drebbel, Robert Fludd, Jean Leurechon, Gaspar Ens, George Philip Hansdorfer, Athanasius Kircher, Oronce Fine, Daniel Schwenter, Gaspar Schott, Jacob Dobrzensky, Isaac and Salomon de Caus, is to list only a few—and those the best known—who show this influence.[169] Not that Hero was the sole influence. Renaissance scholars recaptured much of the Hellenistic tradition, but added to it ideas and developments that were all its own. In 1615 Salomon de Caus, for example, could list as his predecessors in mechanical technology Archimedes, Philo, Hero, Vitruvius, Dürer, Michelangelo,

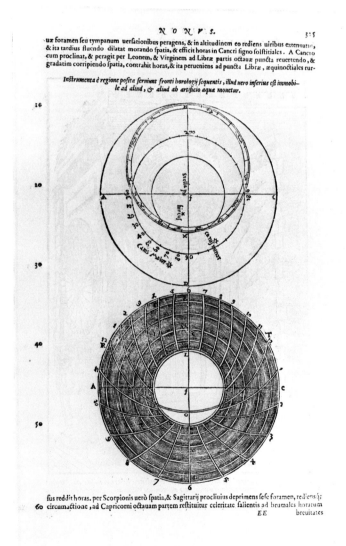

figure 13. Dials of an anaphoric clock. From Barbaro's edition of Vitruvius, *De Architectura . . . ,* 1567, 325.

168. In Thevenot's *Veterum Mathematicae Opera,* 1687.
169. For detailed discussions of Hero's influence, see Boas, and de Rochas, 77–175.

breuitates. Quæ sunt in horologiorum descriptionibus rationes, & apparatus, ut sint ad usum ex-
peditiores quàm aptissimè potui præscripsi. Restat nunc de machinationibus, & de earum princi-
pijs ratiocinari. Itaque de his, ut corpus emendatum Architecturæ perficiatur, in sequenti uolumi-
ne incipiam scribere.

Aquæ temperatio in hoc horologio artificiosissimè fit, & difficultatem habet non mediocrem. Cæterum
in magnis uoluisse satis. & forte non longe aberrabimus ab intentione Vitruuiana. Esto igitur post frontem
horologij aquæ conceptaculum præparatum, hoc Vitruuio est castellum, in quod aqua per fistulam influit.
Sub castello foramen est paruum, ut effluere possit aqua. ei foramini tympanum est adnexum, in quo etiam 60
est

Raphael, Petrus Ramus, Oronce Fine, Jacques Besson, and Ramelli. The list is an interesting one, and in the works of many of the men listed, as in those previously mentioned, water-clocks, usually of the inflow type, are to be found. Particularly important were the descriptions of water-clocks in Vitruvius (figs. 12–14), which are naturally placed among the various kinds of machines that an architect would be expected to understand. Vitruvius' book was edited and translated several times in the 16th and 17th centuries, but exactly what effect it and the Heronic treatises had on the everyday activities of practical engineers awaits investigation.[170] Heronic devices were, however, proposed and were made. The most famous examples perhaps are those of the automata erected in the gardens of the great villas around Rome,[171] and of the Villa d'Este at Tivoli.[172] As in the Middle Ages, some knowledge of these wonders was transmitted to a wider public in popular romances. Thus we have in Thomas Nashe's novel, *The Unfortunate Traveller* (1594),[173] a description of an artificial paradise. Elsewhere, Nashe gives us some idea of what was familiar to Elizabethans in the way of mechanical marvels. He mentions Archimedes' sphere, dancing balls, artificial flies, 'an egge shell that shall clyme up to the top of a speare.'[174] Some of these devices would have been spring driven, but some relied upon water. More mundanely, in 1582 Thomas Bedwell, charged with the repair of Dover Harbour, sent a memorandum to the Queen's Council mentioning 'things...never before used or remembered; construction of sluices; to make a clock to go by water continually without setting.'[175] We do not know if Bedwell's clock was ever built. Nor do we know how often the clepsydrae described in works of mechanical imagination by men such as Oronce Fine [176] (fig. 15), Salomon de Caus,[177] Fausto Veranzio,[178] John Bate,[179] or Jacob Dobrzensky[180] were turned from printed word into wood and metal, and erected to adorn gentlemen's gardens. Certainly the literary tradition is a strong one, and combined with the clear evidence we have that other forms of Heronic

figure 14 (opposite). Anaphoric clock. From Barbero's edition of Vitruvius, *De Architectura . . . ,* 1567, 326.

170. See, however, for some indications, Gille (II) 186–7, Keller (I) *passim. Cf.* for Vitruvius, the large-scale claims of Yates.

171. de Beer (I).

172. de Beer (II). For a variety of other examples of mechanical marvels, see Keller (II).

173. In McKerrow, iii, 282–5.

174. *Summer's Last Will and Testament,* 1600, in *Ibid.,* iii, 235.

175. *Calendar State Papers: Domestic,* cliii, April 1582, no. 27. Dover Harbour was extensively rebuilt between 1583 and 1586. There are a series of memoranda about it in the state papers. See also Scott, and Harris, 11–35. For Bedwell, see *Notes & Queries,* 2nd ser., x, 29, 18, 74. It is perhaps significant that in at least two of his projects Bedwell was associated with Italian engineers.

176. *Protomathesis,* Paris, 1532.

177. *Les Raisons des Forces Mouvantes avec diverses Machines tant Utilles que plaisantes. Aus quelles sont adioints plusiers desseings de grotes et fontaines,* Frankfurt, 1615, Bk. I, problems vii & viii.

178. *Machinae Novae Fausto Veranti Siceni cum declaratione Latine Italica, Hispanica, Gallica, et Germanica,* Venice, 1595 & 1615.

179. *The Mysterys of Nature and Art. Contained in foure severall Tretises . . . partly Collected, and partly of the Authors peculiar Practise and Invention,* London, 1634.

180. *Nova, et Amaenior de admirando Fontium genio (ex abditis naturae claustris, in orbis lucem emanante) Philosophia,* Ferrara, 1657, 1659.

devices were made and used, it is not unlikely that classical forms of water-clock were also brought into use. Certainly one of the peaks of this tradition, Claude Perrault's great French translation with commentary of Vitruvius' *de Architectura,* had some influence.[181]

figure 15. Clepsydra with float in the form of a ship. From Oronce Fine, *de Horologiis Solaribus . . . ,* 1560, 192.

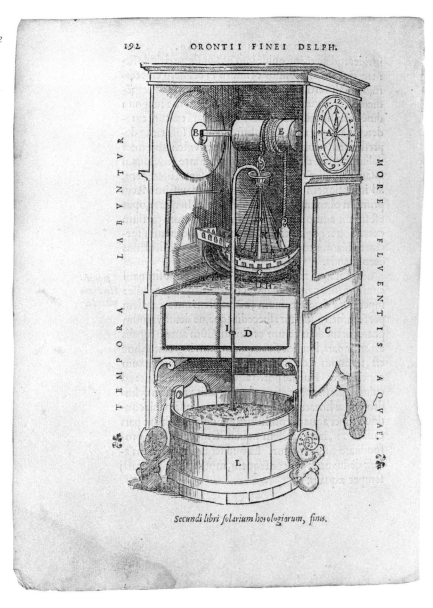

181. E.g. on Guillaume Amontors, see below. The full title of the work was *Les Dix Livres d'Architecture de Vitruve. Corrigez et Traduits nouvellement en Français, avec des Notes et des Figures par M. Perrault,* Paris, 1679 (2nd rev. & enl. edit., 1684).

Compartmented Cylindrical Clepsydrae

The fourth of the main classes of clepsydrae consists of those which use a compartmented cylinder. Although among the best-documented of water-clocks, their origins are unknown. The earliest known evidence comes from Isḥāq b. Sīd's description in the *Libros del Saber* (1276/7)[182] (fig. 11). Although this context suggests an immediate origin in Islam, for which there is a little evidence,[183] the ultimate origin of the device is less obvious. It may, as Price has suggested,[184] be involved with the Indian and Islamic tradition of mercury-powered perpetual-motion wheels. Isḥāq b. Sīd's contrivance was simple but ingenious. In order to obtain an even drive to turn an astrolabe plate, he constructed a drum, the interior of which was divided into twelve compartments. In the wall of each compartment there was a small hole. Into the drum was inserted sufficient mercury to just fill half the compartments. The drum itself was mounted on a large wheel round which was a weight drive. An arbor from this wheel led to a pinion which meshed with the geared edge of the astrolabe dial. In operation, the pull of the weight on the wheel was counteracted by the gradual trickle of the mercury from one compartment inside the drum to the next, thus giving a slow, controlled, and regulated motion to the turning of the astrolabe (fig. 11).

That Isḥāq b. Sīd ever made his clock is not known. Nor is what influence it had, if any, on succeeding generations of Spanish clockmakers. Since the treatise was written in the vernacular Castilian and not in Latin, its possible influence elsewhere in Europe was greatly limited, but there must have been some since an Italian translation of it was included by Gueruccio Federighi in a *Trattato della Sfera* which he wrote at Florence in 1341.[185] Thereafter darkness descends, although we know that the manuscript itself ultimately came into the hands of Giovambatista Strozzi (1551–1634), in whose inventory for 1612 it appears, and in the library of whose heirs it remained until 1738.[186]

The principle of the compartmented cylindrical clepsydra reappeared in Europe in 1598 in an intentionally obscure tract by Attilio Parisio,[187] describing a silent clock with only one wheel that he claimed to have invented. His device consisted of a compartmented clepsydra driving a dial (as in an anaphoric clock) which carried two

---

182. See above, p. 29. We may also note here that White (I), 120–1, and Combridge (IV) & (V) have interpreted the 'King Hezekiah' clock as of compartmental cylinder form.

183. I.e. the use of mercury in balance arms by Khalaf al-Murādī noted above, p. 20.

184. Price (II), 101–2. *Cf.* the comments by Burgess, 399 ff, on the list of water instruments in the *Sūrya-Siddhânta.*

185. Bedini (I), on which much of this section depends.

186. It is now in the Biblioteca Apostolica Vaticana, Codice 8174.

187. *Discorso Dell'Eccell. D. di Leggi, Il Sr Attilio Parisio. Sopra la sua Nuova Inventione d'Horologi con una sola Ruota. Nel quale si dimostra la real essentia loro, le qualità, i moti & effetti maraviglioso, insieme con le risolutioni di quante oppositioni gli potessero esser fatte,* Venice, 1598.

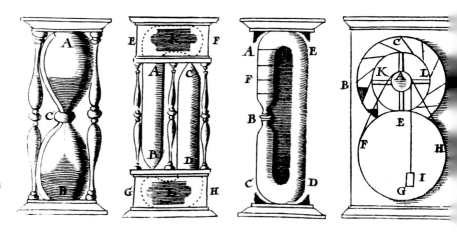

figure 16. Three siphon clepsydrae and a compartmented clepsydra. From Gaspar Schott, *Technica Curiosa . . .* , 1644, pl. vii, figs. 35–38.

discs, one with hour numerals marked in a sunburst, the other showing the current astrological sign. These were read through two semicircular slots cut in a frontplate which concealed the rest of the mechanism. The clock also had a striking mechanism, as had that of Isḥāq b. Sīd. Whether Parisio had any knowledge of the similar device described in the *Libros del Saber* when he began his own work is unknown. He claims to have spent fourteen years and much money developing the device, suggesting he did not. In Bedini's reconstruction, moreover, Parisio's device has only one division within the drum, a considerable difference from his predecessor's.

Be this as it may, Parisio's clock was certainly made, one example being presented to Pope Clement VIII. This was seen in 1612 by Angelo Rocca[188] and in 1681 by an Abate Lancelloti.[189] Parisio also claimed to have presented one to the Grand Duke of Tuscany, although no trace of this example has yet been found. The clock clearly aroused some interest, and in 1626 an attempt was made to remedy the deficiencies of Parisio's description, by an anonymous author writing at Treviso.[190] His work, however, remained unpublished, and it was not until 1648 that a detailed description of the compartmented cylindrical clepsydra was printed by Mario Bettini[191] (1582–1657). This description was immediately reissued, with additions by Francesco Eschinardi (1623–1700),[192] and it was through these publications that the principle of the device first became widely known. As usual the situation is complicated by the

188. Angelo Rocca, *de Companis Commentarius . . . in uo multa non minus admiratione, ac scitu digna, quam lectu incurda in ecclesia Dei Reperiri narrator . . .* , Rome, 1612.
189. Bedini (I), 124.
190. Honeyman Ms 91, now in a private collection in Paris. A facsimile edition with translation and commentary is being prepared by Silvio A. Bedini and A.J. Turner. For a short description, see Sotheby, no. 1251.
191. *Aerarii Philosophiae Mathematicae . . .* Bononie, 1648. 'Epinomis post partem II, Tomi II . . .' (separately paginated) 45–60. For an early example of the clock being made following Bettini's description in the *Aeraria . . .* , see Plot, 240. The clock belonged to Sir Anthony Cope of Hanwell Castle, who subsequently made further experiments with it.
192. *Horologium Hydraulicum ex Aerario P Marii Bettini cum Appendice P. Francesco Eschinardi, . . .* n.p., n.d., and in Bettini's *Apiaria Philosophiae Mathematicae . . .* , 1650 & 1654. It was also included in *Schiaro de' Letterati di Roma,* 1672. An abridged English translation of Bettini and Eschinardi's account was included in Venatus Mandey & Joseph Moxon, *Mechanick-Powers: or the Mystery of Nature and Art Unvail'd,* London, 1696, 219–27.

possibility of independent invention. Neither Bettini nor Eschinardi show any awareness of Parisio's tract, nor in 1656, when the Campani brothers developed a similar timepiece for Pope Alexander VII using mercury instead of water, is there any indication that anyone, apart from themselves, had ever conceived of it.[193] A comparable lack of historical perspective was also shown by Domenico Martinelli (who admittedly disclaimed originality for the pieces he described), who in 1669 provided the most exhaustive description of different types of clepsydra depending upon the compartmented cylinder principle.[194] Included among them was the form which, whether independently redeveloped by the Maurist Benedictine monk Charles Vailly who had been stimulated by Gaspar Schott's description of a compartmented cylindrical sand-clock[195] (fig. 16), or derived more directly from Italy, was to become widespread in 18th-century France and elsewhere. This type may be most conveniently referred to as the falling-drum clepsydra.

The falling-drum clepsydra essentially consists of an upright

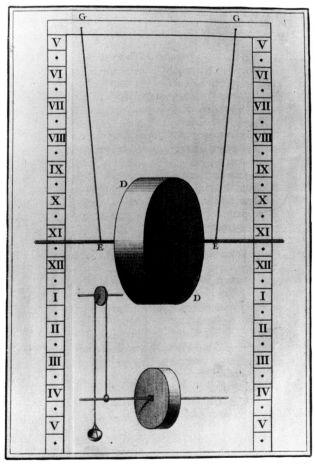

figure 17. Plan of a falling-drum compartmented clepsydra. From Jacques Alexandre, *Traité Général des Horloges,* Paris, 1734, 86.

193. Bedini (I), 127–30.
194. A translation of the work was included by Jacques Ozanam in his *Recreations Mathematiques,* Paris, 1694, and many later editions.
195. Alexandre, 73–5 & 291–2. Schott described the device in *Technica Curiosa sive Mirabilia Artis libris xii,* Nuremburg, 1664, Bk. ix, ch. ix, fig. 38. A related device using sand is shown in Archangelo Maria Radi, *Nuova Scienza di Horologi a Polvere che mostrano, e suonano distintamente tutte l'Hore,* Rome, 1665, which should also be considered in this context. For Vailly and Alexandre, see [Tassin].

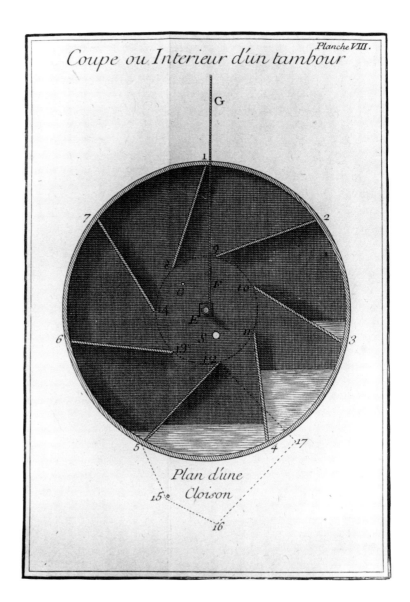

Plan d'une Cloison

figure 18. Section of a drum
of a compartmented cylindrical
clepsydra. From Jacques
Alexandre, *Traité Général des
Horloges,* Paris, 1734, 82.

figure 19 (opposite). An 18th-century
clepsydra workshop. From
Salmon, *l'Art du Potier d'étain,* Paris,
1788, pl. 26. (Photograph:
the British Library, London)

rectangular architectural frame which is open in the centre and has
hours marked down each side (catalogue no. 6 & fig. 17). A compartmented drum is supported in the open centre on two cords,
wound around the arbor of the drum. This arbor is extended to cut
the hour scale on each side. Under its own weight the drum is free
to revolve slowly down the cords, and if the quantity of water within
and the sizes of the cords and of the orifices are properly adjusted, it
will indicate the time on the hour scales at the sides. Such clocks
were also sometimes furnished with striking-work and with alarms
(fig. 19). Throughout the 18th and 19th centuries, especially in agricultural regions, the falling-drum clepsydra in its various forms was
extremely popular as a cheap and reliable timekeeper. Manufactured not by clock-makers, but by pewterers and tin-plate makers
(fig. 19), the centre for their production in France was at Sens in
Burgundy and to a lesser extent at Chartres.[196] They were also

196. Salmon, 132. At 133–5 Salmon gives a detailed account of the manufacture of these water-
clocks 'très exacte & d'un pris très-modique.'

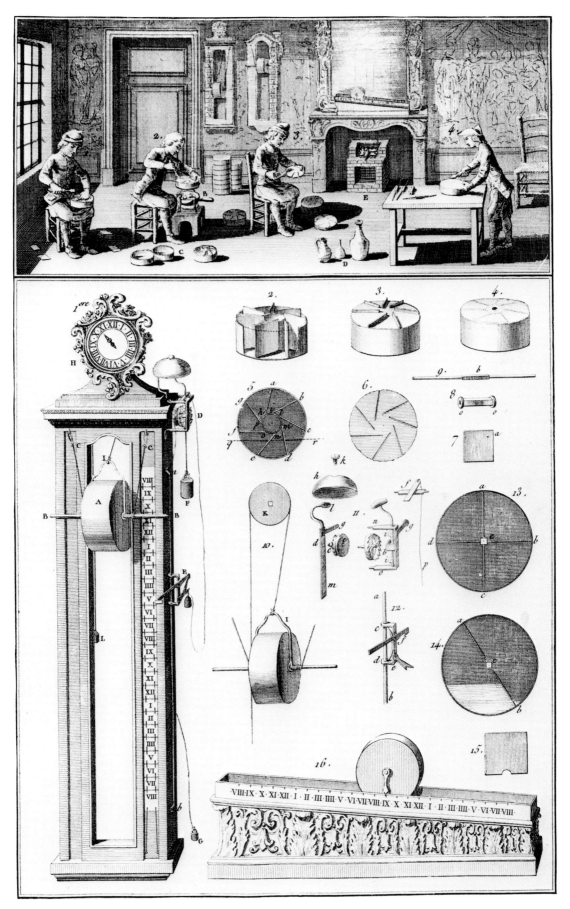

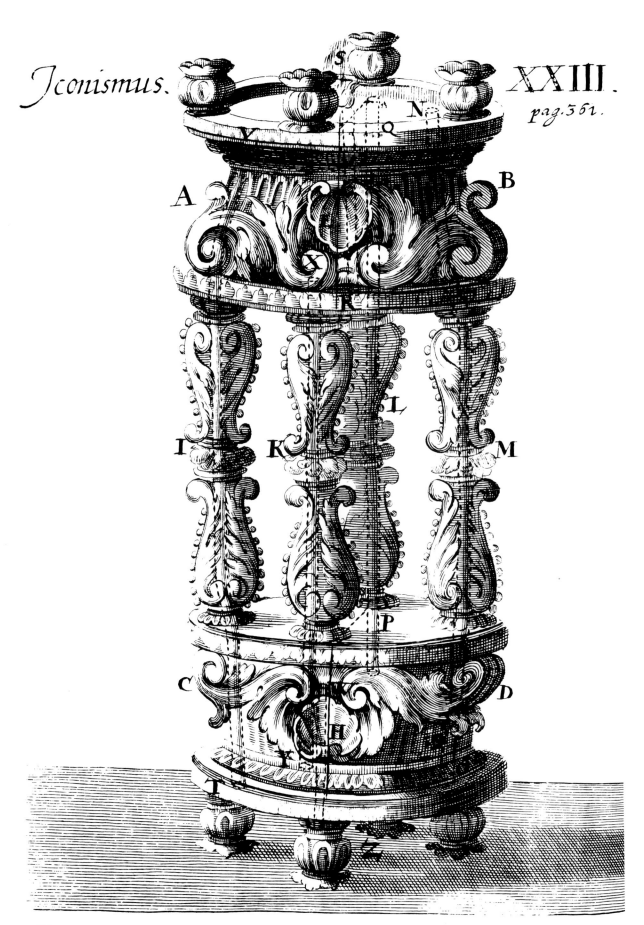

made in London and in Germany, for in 1752 the unidentified M.G.B.H. published at Halle his *Ausführliche und Vollständige Abhandlung von Wasseruhren . . .* a treatise which seems to be based on practical experience.[197] Once evidently in common use, they must have been both attractive and reliable when newly painted and well-maintained. In a variant form the drum was placed on an inclined plane, which it gradually descended, and small mantel or table models were developed with their mechanisms entirely contained within the case.[198] Examples of all these, however, are now extremely rare.[199]

Although the most successful, the compartmented cylindrical clepsydra was not the only form to be developed and made during the Renaissance. Two examples of an Heronian siphon-operated table clepsydra similar in form to a sand-glass have survived[200] and in the late 17th and 18th centuries there were suggestions by *savants* and *amateurs* for improved forms of water-clocks, the stimulus in many cases being Perrault's comments on the clepsydra in his edition of Vitruvius. Certainly this was the starting place for Guillaume Amontons (1663–1705), who in 1695 described an ingenious new form which seems to have been a by-product of his work on thermometers[201] (fig. 21). More important was Perrault's own invention of a pendulum-controlled clepsydra with two vertical water-wheels, the principle of which has been successfully re-used in recent years.[202] In 1733, M. du Quet submitted a water-clock to the Académie Royale des Sciences at Paris,[203] while a version with a simple floating siphon invented by Lieutenant Baussard in 1790 has survived.[204] In 1835, Charles F. Partington described an unoriginal form of clepsydra which he had presented to the 'National Repository'[205] and between 1855 and 1900 at least ten British patents were taken out for 'liquid clocks'. By this time, however, hydraulic horology was little more than an inventor's sport and a subject for nostalgic antiquarianism, a fact fully exploited in the early decades of the

197. Two London examples by Arnold Finchett, father and son, are preserved in the British Museum, Dept. of Medieval and Later Antiquities. For M.G.B.H., see Baillie, 231–4.

198. An example of the inclined-plane type is shown in Salmon's illustration of a clepsydra manufactory (fig. 19). The table model is described by Martinelli, 54–7 and Ozanam, *Recreations Mathematiques,* Paris, 1694, 505–8. For an example, perhaps Italian, see Chayette-Sabrier, lot 261.

199. Thus even in 1890 Planté, 24 could remark '. . . les amateurs étrangers et . . . les fondeurs du cuillers lui ont fait, chacun dans un but différent, une telle chasse que l'on parvient difficilement a en trouver les spécimens.' (Foreign collectors and . . . spoon-casters each for a different end have made such a hunt after it that one succeeds with difficulty to find examples of them.)

200. In the National Maritime Museum, Greenwich, and the Musée Nationale de la Renaissance, Ecouen. See Bedini (IV), 25–52.

201. G. Amontons, *Remarques et Experiences Phisiques sur la construction d'une nouvelle clepsidre, sur les Baromètres, Termomètres & Higromètres,* Paris, 1695.

202. 'Horloge à pendule qui va par le moyen de l'Eau,' *Receuil des Machines approuvées par l'Academie,* no. 17, 39–44, and see below, cat. no. 7.

203. *Ibid.,* no. 408, 131–2.

204. C.N.A.M., 84–5, no. 7496. It is inscribed 'Horloge nocturne inventée et exécutée par M. Baussard Ancien Lieutenant de Fregate. Attaché aux classes en l'année 1790.' and at the bottom of the scale, 'Dedié a l'Académie Royale des Sciences an 1791.'

205. Partington, i, 317.

figure 20 (opposite). Siphon-operated table fountain from Gaspar Schott, *Technica Curiosa . . . ,* 1644, pl. 23, 361.

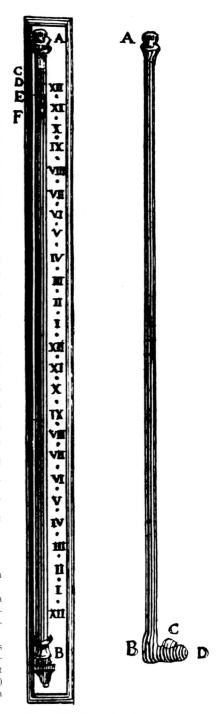

figure 21. Clepsydra from Guillaume Amontons, *Remarques et Expériences Phisiques sur la construction d'une nouvelle clepsidre, sur les Baromètres, Termomètres & Higromètres,* Paris, 1695.

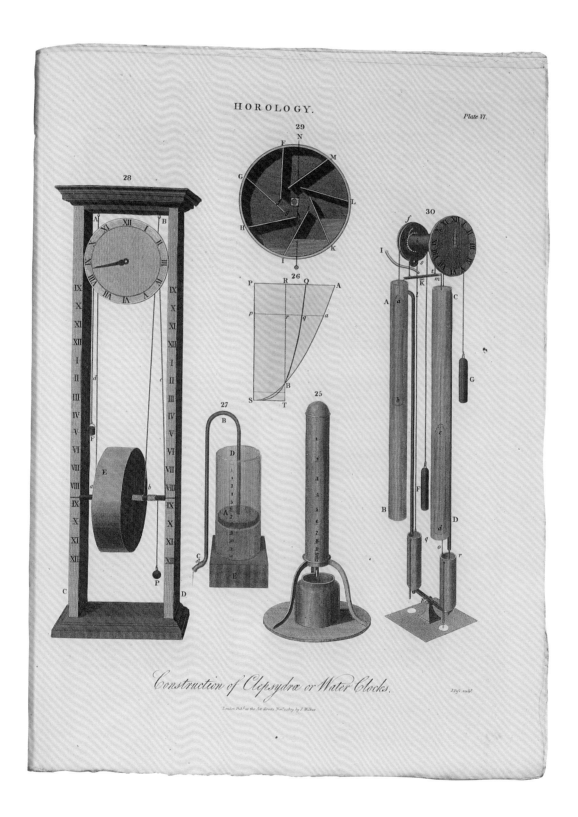

Construction of Clepsydræ or Water Clocks.

figure 22. Modern clepsydrae.
Pl. II in 'Clepsydra,' in Rees' *The
Cyclopaedia; or Universal
Dictionary of Arts, Sciences, and
Literature,* London, 1819–20.

20th century with the manufacture of a series of imitation 17th-century water-clocks.[206] The high tradition of the clepsydra had clearly come to an end.[207]

206. By the Pearson Page Co., Birmingham, England.
207. An exception, however, should be made for the remarkable water-clock with free pendulum designed by the Earl of Meath between 1899 and 1906 and still (in 1958) working at Kilroddry Castle, County Wicklow, Ireland. See Lloyd, i, 138–40.

Water-clocks Catalogue

1. Facsimile of an Egyptian Clepsydra

c. 1400 B.C. (original)
c. A.D. 1970 (facsimile)
Plaster
Diameter of rim 19½ in. (495 mm)
Diameter of base 10¾ in. (273 mm)
Height 14 in. (356 mm)
Not signed
Inventory 32

The clepsydra is of the outflow type originally graduated on the inner wall and with a small hole set in the wall just above the base. Almost certainly this orifice would originally have been surmounted by the figure of a dog-headed ape, the emblem of Thoth, god of wisdom and the moon.[208] The walls are inclined to the base at an angle of approximately 110°, and are decorated in three bands. The lowest of these is divided into six compartments and shows King Amenhotep III with the twelve moon gods, two to each compartment. In the middle band are the circumpolar stars and images of the deities of the days of the week. Opposite the orifice is a large panel extending from the middle to the upper band in which the king is depicted protected by Thoth and offering sacrifice to the sun god Harmachis. The remainder of the upper band contains symbols of the planets and the constellations through which the sun passes in the course of the year.[209]

Since the hours of the Egyptian day and night were unequal, the length of an hour varied according to the season of the year. The twelve months were, therefore, marked on the rim of the vessel and a separate hour scale marked down the side for each.[210] In use, the orifice at the base was opened and the hour read off from the changing level of the water against the appropriate month scale. At the top of the vessel a line was marked round the inner wall to indicate the level to which it should be filled. This is no longer visible in the Karnak clepsydra and is not, therefore, shown in the facsimile.

The original clepsydra, from which the present example is copied, was discovered in a refuse pit during excavations at the Amon Temple, Karnak by G. Legrain in 1904. Later reassembled, it is made of translucent alabaster, the outer surface decorated with coloured stones and faience inlay.[211] Its rate of flow was approximately ten drops per second.

208. Sloley, 44, who cites Horapollo (? 5th century A.D.), *Hieroglyphica* (1548) i, 16. '. . . in hydrologis suis Aegyptia Cynocephalum sedentem pingunt, ex membro vero ejus aquam affluentem faciunt.' (The ape was peculiarly appropriate on a clepsydra, apart from its association with Thoth, because it was thought to urinate twelve times a day at regular intervals.) For surviving monkeys, see cat. no. 2 and illustrations in Pogo, 403–25.
209. For the relation of these decorations to astronomical temple ceilings, see Pogo, 418–20.
210. The proportions between the lengths of the longest and shortest scales, 12:14, agree with those given in the inscription of Amenemhet (Sloley, 45). A method of calculating the scales is found on part of a leaf of a papyrus book among the Oxyrhynchus Papyri. See Grenfell & Hunt, no. 470 11, 31–87, and discussion in Sloley, 45–6.
211. See Daressy; Borchardt, 6–7. A cast of the clepsydra is in The Science Museum, London, to which it was presented by the Egyptian government in 1923. Ward, pt. II, no. 4, 8. (See also pl. I in pt. I.) Another facsimile is in the Uhrenmuseum, Wuppertal, W. Germany. See Abeler, 8.

figure 23. Catalogue no. 1:
Facsimile of an Egyptian clepsydra.

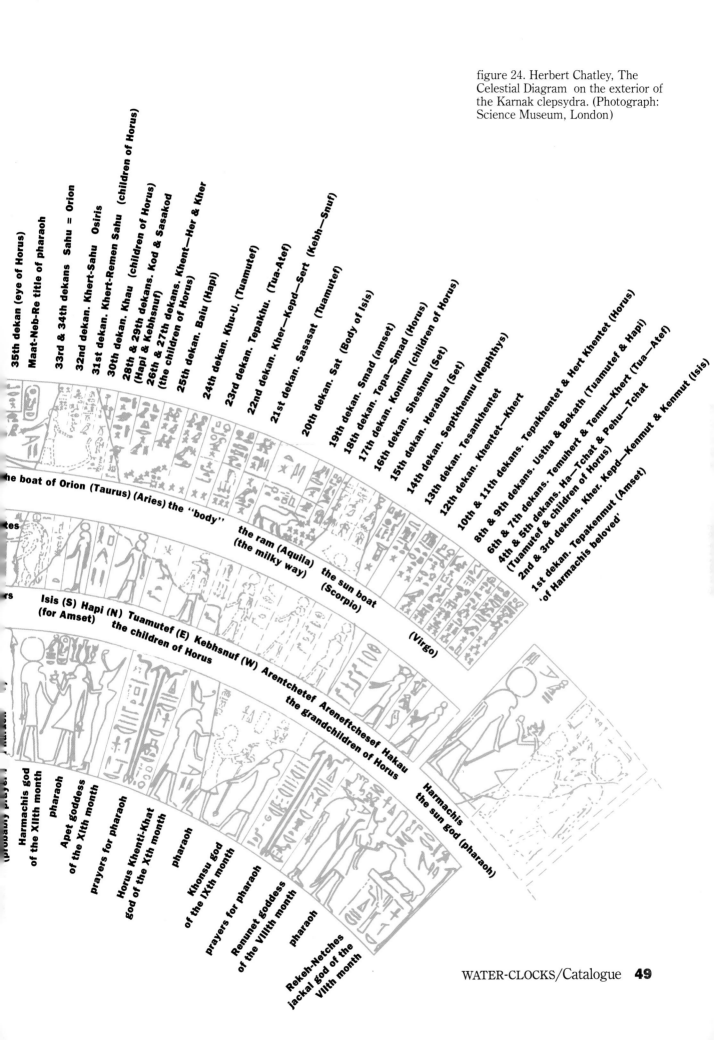

figure 24. Herbert Chatley, The Celestial Diagram on the exterior of the Karnak clepsydra. (Photograph: Science Museum, London)

35th dekan (eye of Horus)
Maat-Neb-Re title of pharaoh
33rd & 34th dekans Sahu = Orion
32nd dekan. Khert-Sahu Osiris
31st dekan. Khert-Remen Sahu (children of Horus)
30th dekan. Khau (children of Horus)
28th & 29th dekans. Kod & Sasakod (Hapi & Kebhsnuf)
26th & 27th dekans. Khent—Her & Kher (the children of Horus)
25th dekan. Baiu (Hapi)
24th dekan. Khu-U. (Tuamutef)
23rd dekan. Tepakhu. (Tua-Atef)
22nd dekan. Kher—Kepd—Sert (Kebh—Snuf)
21st dekan. Sasasat (Tuamutef)
20th dekan. Sat (Body of Isis)
19th dekan. Smad (amset)
18th dekan. Tepa—Smad (Horus)
17th dekan. Konimu (children of Horus)
16th dekan. Sheshmu (Set)
15th dekan. Herabua (Set)
14th dekan. Septkhennu (Nephthys)
13th dekan. Tesankhentet
12th dekan. Khentet—Khert
10th & 11th dekans. Tepakhentet & Hert Khentet (Horus)
8th & 9th dekans. Ustha & Bekath (Tuamutef & Hapi)
6th & 7th dekans. Temuhert & Temu—Khert (Tua—Atef)
4th & 5th dekans. Ha—Tchat & Pehu—Tchat (Tuamutef & children of Horus)
2nd & 3rd dekans. Kher. Kepd—Kenmut & Kenmut (Isis)
1st dekan. Tepakenmut (Amset)
'of Harmachis beloved'

the boat of Orion (Taurus) (Aries) the "body"
the ram (Aquila) (the milky way) the sun boat (Scorpio)
(Virgo)

Isis (S) Hapi (N) Tuamutef (E) Kebhsnuf (W) Arentchetef Areneftchesef Hakau
(for Amset) the children of Horus the grandchildren of Horus

Harmachis the sun god (pharaoh)

Harmachis god of the XIIth month
Apet goddess of the XIth month
pharaoh
prayers for pharaoh
Horus Khenti-Khat god of the Xth month
pharaoh
Khonsu god of the IXth month
prayers for pharaoh
Renunet goddess of the VIIIth month
pharaoh
Rekeh-Netches jackal god of the VIIth month

WATER-CLOCKS/Catalogue **49**

2. Facsimile of a Romano-Egyptian Clepsydra

c. A.D. 100 (original)
c. A.D. 1970 (facsimile)
Plaster
Overall height 15 in. (381 mm)
Interior diameter 6⅝ in. (168 mm)
Inventory 33

The cylindrical vessel has a small aperture in the wall slightly above the base. Above this orifice on the outside is a figure of a seated dog-headed ape. The original of this cast was found during excavations at Edfu (the ancient *Atbō, Apollinopolis Magna*, a capital of Upper Egypt) in 1901. It is made of white limestone, and is now in the Museum of Egyptian Antiquities, Cairo.[212]

Of the exact nature of this clepsydra there is some doubt. Most commentators have followed Borchardt and Sloley[213] in considering it to be an inflow clepsydra for use at night. At dusk the orifice would be closed and water would be poured into the instrument up to the level of the lowest hour line. Further water would then be allowed to drip into the vessel at a regulated rate from a reservoir (which would have to be compensated for change of pressure). A direct reading of the hour from the interior scales would not, however, have been possible since, according to Borchardt, the lower hour lines are not visible and the others only partially so. Even if they were, the fact that water drips into the vessel would make assessing the level difficult. Borchardt suggests that a second hollow cylinder sat above the first, graduated on the exterior, and that a float in the lower cylinder carried a marker which passed through the seating of the second cylinder to indicate the hour on the outside of the upper cylinder.

An interpretation in some ways simpler than this was proposed by Sir William Flinders Petrie.[214] Noting that the hour lines are uniform at the top of the vessel, he suggested that it was an outflow clepsydra in which was placed a solid cone, tapering parabolically and with base equal to the internal diameter to provide pressure compensation. The largest divisions in the scales being for September and the shortest for March proved, he suggested, that the scales were compensated for temperature variation, not for the seasons. This suggestion, however, did not appeal to Pogo[215] who, hypothesizing that the original form of inflow clepsydrae was prismatic and cylindrical examples a later development, thought that the scales on the Edfu example had been inaccurately copied from an earlier specimen. In the absence of further evidence it seems unlikely that

212. For a detailed discussion, see Borchardt, 22–5.
213. Sloley, 48–9.
214. Note by F[linders] P[etrie] appended to Sloley, 50.
215. Pogo, 412.

figure 25. Catalogue no. 2:
Facsimile of a Roman-Egyptian clepsydra.
Side view.

the disagreement can be resolved. However, if the clepsydra really functioned in the manner described by Borchardt (with a second upper cylinder to indicate the hours), there seems no reason why the hour lines should have been marked on the interior of the lower cylinder where they are redundant. Secondly, if the symbolical explanation of the presence of the dog-headed ape be correct, then one might expect the orifice associated with it to have a function in the time measurement, and not to be merely an emptying valve.[216] Two plain cones approximating the parabolic form required by Petrie's theory survive among the Egyptological collections at University College, London.[217] Another cast of the Edfu clepsydra has been in The Science Museum, London, since 1923.[218]

figure 26. Catalogue no. 2. Top view.

216. Doubts that the Edfu clepsydra is of the inflow type also seem to have been felt by Thureau-Dangin, 133–6.
217. Sloley & Petrie, 16–7.
218. Ward, no. 6, 8. Another facsimile is in the Uhrenmuseum, Wuppertal, W. Germany, Abeler 8.

3. Reconstruction of a Sinking-bowl Water-clock

Beaten copper
Diameter of reservoir 18¼ in. (464 mm)
Diameter of sinking bowl 12½ in. (318 mm)
Not signed
Inventory D1004

The semicircular tank on three cast feet would normally be kept filled with water. The smaller hemispherical bowl has a hole pierced in its centre to act as an orifice. This orifice was sometimes made from gold or hard stone which would better resist erosion caused by the constant passage of water. The bowl was floated on top of the water in the tank and would gradually sink, the rate of sinking being controlled by the size of the orifice. An attendant who watched the water-clock would give an aural time signal and refloat the bowl each time it submerged completely.

Provenance: Hagans Clock Manor Museum, Evergreen, Colorado.

figure 27. Catalogue no. 3:
Reconstruction of a sinking-bowl
water-clock.

4. Reconstruction of a Romano-Greek Water-clock

A.D. 1982
Walnut, oak, iron, copper and canvas
Overall height 78 in. (1981 mm)
Case by Sofus Sorenson, Rockford
Figure carved by Yousta Johnson, Rockford
Canvas dial by Karen McCauley, Rockford
Not signed
Inventory 369

A cylindrical drum is mounted vertically on a pedestal which contains the water machinery. The drum is divided vertically into columns representing the zodiacal signs, which are marked round the base. Crossing these columns horizontally are twenty-four curved hour lines. Also carried on the pedestal are two miniature figures, one (a satyr) holding a pointer, the other (a cupid) crying.

The reconstruction shown here is a composite model that encapsulates much of the history of the inflow clepsydra. It follows the reconstruction by Claude Perrault[219] of a clepsydra of Ctesibios of Alexandria, according to the description given by Vitruvius.[220] The model has, therefore, a very limited resemblance to Ctesibios' original conception, the hydraulic arrangements of which are likely to have been simpler.[221]

The interior mechanism of Perrault's machine is as follows. Beneath the figure of the crying cupid is a pipe which leads water from an external source into its body and causes its tears. These drop into a basin at his feet, whence they are led through an horizontal pipe in the top of the pedestal into a vertical cylinder beneath the pointing figure. Inside this cylinder is a float to which the pointing figure is connected. As the water level rises, therefore, the figure is gradually lifted higher up the cylinder, against which it indicates the hour with its pointer. At the end of twenty-four hours, when the float tube is full and the figure at its highest point, water from the float tube overflows into a siphon that operates to release the water into a compartmented water-wheel with six divisions and which thus makes one complete revolution in six days. The water-wheel has a six-leaved pinion which turns a wheel of sixty, which in turn, through a pinion of ten leaves, turns a wheel of sixty-one. This is attached to the central shaft of the hour column, which thus makes one complete revolution in 366 days. By so doing, the appropriate part of the columns of zodiacal signs is presented to the pointer, and the curved hour lines enable the unequal hours to be shown.

Born at Paris, Claude Perrault (1613–1688) — one of four brothers who all attained distinction — was given a scientific education studying medicine, anatomy, and mathematics. Following a request from

figure 28. Claude Perrault's conception of Vitruvius' form of the clepsydra of Ctesibios. From *Les Dix Livres d'Architecture,* 2nd edit., Paris, 1684, 56 & 289.

219. Perrault, 288–9. The first edition appeared in 1673.
220. *De Architectura libri decem,* Bk. ix; 508.
221. A reconstruction similar to the present one may be seen in the Uhrenmuseum, Wuppertal, W. Germany, Abeler 9.

figure 29. Catalogue no. 4:
Reconstruction of a
Romano-Greek water-clock.

Colbert to translate Vitruvius, he began a study of this author and of architecture, which became the main preoccupation of his life. A member of the Académie Royale des Sciences virtually from its foundation, Perrault was responsible for the design of the Paris Observatory (1667). Soon afterwards, the design of the Louvre, already begun, was thrown open to competition. Perrault submitted plans which were unanimously adopted. It is largely his design, executed in collaboration with Charles Lebrun (1617–1690) and Giovanni Bernini (1598–1680), which formed the building as it exists today.

In addition to the Louvre, which remains his masterpiece, Perrault was responsible for a triumphal arch for Louis XIV and several minor works including the chapel of the château at Sceaux, and the water-alley and most of the ornamental vases at Versailles. Apart from his remarkable edition of Vitruvius (first edition 1673, second edition 1684), he wrote several other works on architecture, medicine, and natural history of which the most important are *Ordonnonces des cinq espèces de Colonnes, selon la Méthode des Anciens,* 1683; *Essais de Physiques* (4 vols), 1680–1688; *Memoires pour servir à l'Histoire Naturelle des Animaux,* 1671, 1676; and *Receuil d'un grand nombre des Machines . . .,* 1700, which describes machines for building, water-clocks, and other devices. With his brother Charles (1628–1703), best known for his fairy tales (such as *Cinderella*, contained in his *Contes du Temps-passé,* 1697), Perrault assisted in the preparation of the *Memoires* of the Académie Royale concerning its origins, architecture, and painting. Having practised medicine with success before turning to architecture, he retained an interest in these studies all his life. His death was attributed to his dissection of a camel, which had died of a contagious disease.

5. Reconstruction of Su Song's Astronomical and Time-telling Tower.

A.D. 1088–92 (original)
A.D. 1970 (half-scale model)
Teak and copper
Overall height 17 ft. 8 in. (5.38 m)
Base 9 ft. 6 in. x 9 ft. (2.89 m x 2.74 m)
Diameter of wheel 5 ft. 6 in. (1.68 m)
Tower by Sofus Sorenson, Rockford
Larger figures and armillary sphere by Yousta Johnson, Rockford
Water-wheel and escapement by Barnett & Walls Ltd.,
London, to a specification by J.H. Combridge, Ilford
Inventory 181

The square tower of two storeys has a flat balustraded top on which an armillary sphere is mounted, protected by an open-sided roof structure. The sphere is mounted on a crossed base with inset water-levels and with four supporters in the form of dragons. It consists of meridian, horizon, and equatorial rings, the solstitial colure, the ecliptic, and a polar-mounted declination ring. There is a central sighting tube and a gear ring that connects the intermediate rings of the sphere via a central transmission shaft (within a column decorated with clouds and a tortoise) to the power drive concealed in the tower. Beneath the armillary sphere in an open chamber on the first storey is a celestial globe mounted in a meridian ring in a wooden casing such that only half the globe is visible above the horizon circle. Beneath this is an ornamental pagoda of five storeys each having a central doorway in which wooden jacks appear and give aural and visual indications of time. In the top stage the equal (double) hour of the day is indicated by the striking of bells and drums, while the time is exhibited by the jacks in the second stage. At the third level, jacks indicate the *ke*, the hundred divisions into which the twelve double hours are divided.[222] In the fourth, the unequal night divisions are sounded on a gong and in the fifth, the night periods are shown. The visual time indications are provided by the appearance of jacks holding tablets on which the appropriate hour is marked.

The remaining space in the tower is occupied by the water-drive, the gear mechanism, and stairs to reach the upper levels. In the back part of the tower (entirely hidden from view in the original, but shown separately in this reconstruction), is a large *noria*-type water-wheel with thirty-six buckets into each of which water pours at a uniform rate from a reservoir maintained at a constant level. From this main driving wheel runs an horizontal axle, or drive-shaft, ending in a pinion which engages with a gear wheel set towards the lower end of the vertical transmission shaft. This shaft passes up

222. Each *ke* therefore was 14 minutes 24 seconds long.

the tower to drive the intermediate rings of the armillary sphere by means of an oblique gear and intermediate pinion. The main time-telling or jackwork shaft is also driven from the transmission shaft through a pair of gears. The celestial globe is driven in similar fashion to the armillary sphere, by an oblique gear and an intermediate pinion at the top of the time-telling shaft. The second function of the time-telling shaft is to rotate six horizontal wheels that carry round the time-indicating jacks.

Since the purpose of Su Song's tower was to simulate the motion of the heavens, it required careful control of the driving force. The mechanism employed for this purpose constituted, in effect, a water escapement. Its operation is as follows: Mounted on the main water-wheel are thirty-six buckets each attached by a horizontal bucket-holder pivoted slightly below the horizontal diameter of the wheel and with a counterweight at the opposite end of the arm to

figure 30 (below). Pictorial reconstruction of Su Song's astronomical tower. figure 31 (opposite). Catalogue no. 5: Reconstruction of Su Song's astronomical tower.

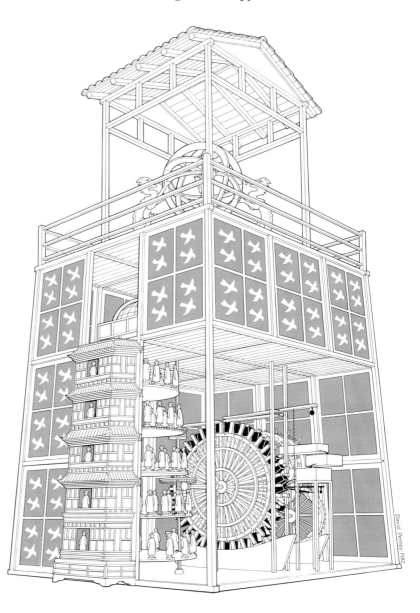

the bucket. Projecting from the bucket itself is a lug. At the beginning of a cycle of action, the water-wheel is held stationary by an horizontal stop that engages the topmost vertical spoke of the wheel. This stop is attached by a short chain to a long balance-lever pivoted on an horizontal axle and with a counterweight at its free end. From the balance-lever a vertical chain passes down to a trip-lever, pivoted at one end, set beneath a counterweighted balance-lever with a forked end through which the chain passes. The sequence of action is then as follows: The main wheel held against the upper stop, water at constant pressure pours into an empty bucket which has arrived below it. As it does so it overcomes the counterweight of the horizontal bucket-holder, and the weight of the water in the bucket is then supported by the lug projecting from the bucket resting against the forked end of the lower balance-lever. When the increased weight of water in the bucket is sufficient to overcome the counterweight of this lower balance-lever, the balance-lever lifts up, releasing the bucket so that its horizontal holder turns around its pivot until the lug engages with the trip-lever beneath. The weight of the full bucket on the trip-lever now works with that of the counterweight on the upper balance-lever to set both levers in motion, thus jerking the upper stop out of engagement with the

32. Action of the escapement of the reconstruction of Su Song's astronomical tower.

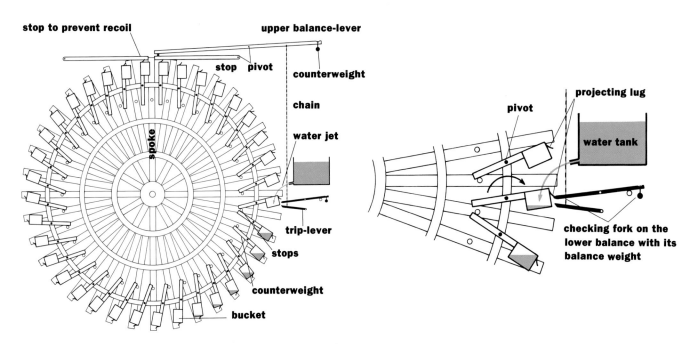

a. The wheel is held against the upper stop and water, at a constant pressure, pours into an empty bucket.

b. The weight of the water overcomes the bucket counterweight and the bucket tips until the projecting lug rests on the checking fork at the end of the lower balance-lever.

wheel spoke. Since the water-wheel is out of balance, thanks to a number of filled or partly filled buckets on its lower right quadrant, it moves down in a clockwise direction. At the same time the two balance-levers return to their normal positions, as does the upper stop, which arrests the wheel at the next spoke. A left-hand stop is provided to prevent recoil. The cycle is completed in 24 seconds; a complete revolution of the wheel thus takes 14 minutes 24 seconds, and 100 revolutions are thus carried out in 24 hours. The water needed to drive Su Song's mechanism was stored in an upper reservoir whence it was delivered to a constant-level tank and so to the buckets. As each bucket descended, its load of water was deposited in a sump, from which place it was lifted again to the upper reservoir by two hand-operated *norias*.[223]

The astronomical tower of Su Song, Han Gonglian, and their associates was built at Kaifeng between 1088 and 1092. When completed it was an imposing structure about 40 feet in height, and it remained in service for some thirty-six years before being carried off into captivity (together with many technicians) by the Jin Tartars. It was rebuilt in Peking, but as its parts gradually wore away they were found impossible to replace, and the device fell out of use.

In addition to the present reconstruction there is a half-size model

223. For translation of Su Song's description of the tower and its mechanism with interpretation, see Needham, Wang Ling, & Price, 28–59. For a closer engineering interpretation, which has been largely followed here, see Combridge (I). See also Needham & Wang Ling (II), 456 ff.

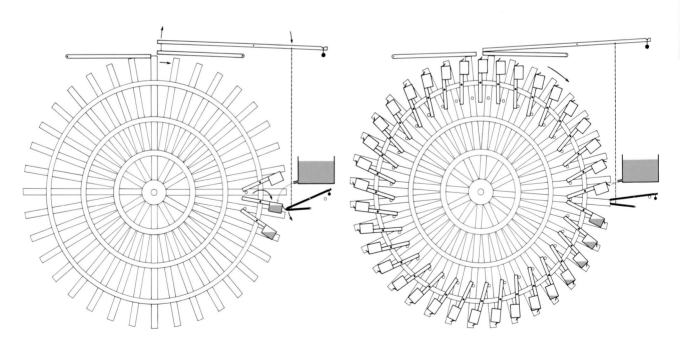

c. Further water in the bucket overcomes the lower balance-lever counterweight. The bucket then falls on the trip-lever, pushing it down. The trip-lever pulls the chain down, raising the upper balance-lever, which in turn jerks the stop-lever upwards, releasing the spoke of the wheel which it held.

d. The wheel turns, bringing the next bucket into the flow of the water. The lower and upper balance-levers return to rest position, allowing the stop-lever to be ready to catch the next spoke of the wheel.

of the escapement system in the City of Liverpool Museum; and one-sixth scale models in The Science Museum, London, and the Uhrenmuseum, Wuppertal (escapement only).[224]

Su Song (A.D. 1020–1101) was born at Nanan in the province of Fujian, and spent his whole life as an imperial civil servant. After passing the provincial examinations in which he came top of the list for an essay on the astronomical basis of the calendar, his first post was Drafting Secretary in the College of All Sages, a scholarly government advisory body. Under the emperor Ying Zong (A.D. 1064–67), he was staff supervisor of the Ministry of Finance and soon afterwards received a decoration as an incorruptible official. In A.D. 1077, Su Song was sent on a diplomatic expedition to the Liao kingdom where his knowledge of astronomical and calendric theory stood him good stead. In A.D. 1089 he was promoted to Vice-Minister of the Ministry of Personnel, and appointed to the Imperial Chancellory. In the following years he received several titles and honours, and was a deputy preceptor to the imperial heir. He died in A.D. 1101.

Su Song is an outstanding example of a cultured and scientifically minded bureaucrat of his time. Apparently associated with the conservative Confucian party, he kept apart from the savage political struggles at the court, devoting himself to literature. Among other works, he wrote a fine study of pharmaceutical botany, zoology, and mineralogy *c.* A.D. 1070, and between A.D. 1090 and 1092 prepared his *Xinyi xiangfa yao* (New Design for a [Mechanized] Armillary [Sphere] and [celestial] Globe), which was presented to the emperor soon afterwards, presumably with the complete machine.[225]

The mechanical design of the astronomical time-telling tower was largely the work of Han Gonglian, whom Su Song found carrying out minor administrative tasks in his own ministry. Together they developed the machine and when its construction was ordered, a committee was established to oversee the work:

> Wang Yuan-Chih [Wang Yuanzhi] Professor at the Public College of Shouchow [Suzhou] formerly Acting Registrar of Yuan-wu [Yuan Wu] in Chêngchow [Zhengzhou] prefecture, should be in charge of construction and the receipt and issue of public materials; while Chou Jih-Yen [Zou Riyan] Director of Astronomical Observations (Southern Region) of the Bureau of Astronomy and Calendar, Yü Thai-Ku [Yu Taigu], Director as Astronomical Observations (Western Region) of the same Bureau, Chang Chung-Hsüan [Zhang Zhong-xuan], Director of Astronomical Observations (Northern Region), and Han Kung-Lien [Han Gonglian] should be appointed to supervise the construction ... the assistants in the Bureau, Yuan Wei-Chi [Yuan Weiji], Miao Ching [Miao Jing], and Chang Tuan [Zhang Duan], and the Superintendent (Chieh-Chi) [Jiei Ji] Liu Chung-Ching [Liu Zhoungjing]; together with the students Hou Yung-Ho [Hou Yonghe] and Yü Tang-Chhen [Yu Dangchen], as investigators of the sun's shadow, the clepsydras, and so on. (Lastly I recommended) the Bureau of Works Foreman Yin Chhing [Yin Qing] to be Clerk of the Works.[226]

figure 33 (opposite). Catalogue no. 5. Water-wheel. figure 34 (above). Catalogue no. 5. Detail of Escapement.

224. For the Liverpool model, see *Antiquarian Horology*, v, 1968, 414–5, and also Combridge (III), 301. For that at Wuppertal, see Abeler, 14–5.
225. This summary is based on the fuller account in Needham, Wang Ling & Price, 5–9.
226. *Hsin I Hsiang Fa Yao* Ch. I. Quoted from Needham & Wang Ling (II), 464.

6. French Falling-drum Clepsydra

Early to mid-19th century
Overall height 44⅜ in. (1127 mm)
Diameter of drum 5¼ (133 mm)
Not signed
Inventory 2669

The rectangular case has a simple semicircular arch over the central opening down which the water-drum descends. On the right-hand side (as seen in the illustration) is a scale of hours drawn in ink directly on the wood and reading 9–12/1–12/1–9. The clepsydra would thus have been reset in either the morning or the evening at about 9 o'clock. Since the divisions, but not the numbers, for the hours are also marked on the left-hand side of the case, it is possible that the clepsydra was originally equipped with paper scales on each side. The frame attached to the upper left-hand side of the case originally contained an alarm activated when the axle of the drum tripped a lever mounted on a frame which could be set against the hour required. Five holes in the left side of the frame against the hours 2 – 5 were probably for this purpose. Alternately this frame may have contained striking-work, but on a relatively plain example such as this, this seems less probable.

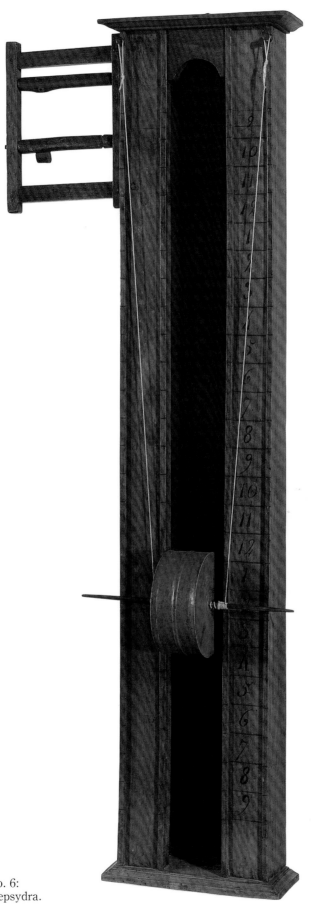

figure 35. Catalogue no. 6:
French falling-drum clepsydra.

7. Swiss Water-clock

1968–9
Plexiglas and aluminum with wood base
Steel alloy pendulum rod
Overall height 37½ in. (952 mm)
Signed: 'H.A. Kuhn, No. 4 Swiss Made'

Inventory 349

figure 36 (opposite). Catalogue no. 7:
Swiss water-clock. Front-view.
figure 37 (opposite, inset).
Catalogue no. 7. Rear view.

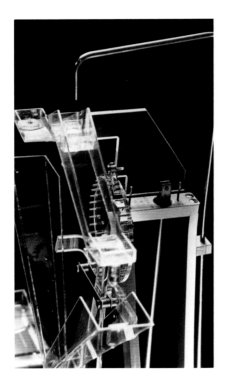

figure 38. Catalogue no. 7.
Escapement.

The 'A'-shaped frame has a horizontal top cross-piece attached to a single column at the back. Through a hole in the cross-piece a pendulum is suspended on a knife edge. Attached to the top of the 'A'-frame is a pin wheel which serves both as an escape wheel and seconds dial. Mounted on the face of this dial is a semicircular detent. A ratchet pawl attached to the pendulum is on the top of the second dial and a click stop, to prevent backlash, is mounted at the bottom of the dial. A vertical oscillating arm, the top of which carries a pin that presses against the detent, is carried on the arbor concentric with the minute and hour dials. Carried on the vertical oscillating arm, at its mid-point, is a double channel (the oscillating channel). Above and below the oscillating channel are inclined fixed channels arranged in a 'V'-shape. There are two sets of double click stops mounted on either side of the 'A'-frame to prevent backlash on the minute and the hour dials. The whole machine is mounted on a wood base that contains the reservoir and an electric pump. A pipe runs from the reservoir to the top of the clock where it returns in an inverted 'U' above the pendulum. Attached to the top of the pendulum is a double inclined channel at the centre of which is a compartment divided into two 'L'-shaped sections and a central double 'L'.

The manner of the operation is as follows. Water is pumped up the pipe from the reservoir and pours into the central compartment of the pendulum channels. The double 'L' controls the quantity of water and ensures that it flows first down a channel on one side of the pendulum and then down the other, thus causing the pendulum to oscillate. On every other swing of the pendulum, the ratchet pawl on the second dial moves the dial one pin. There are forty pins on the second dial, which revolves once every minute. Thus, the pendulum should perform one swing in ⅔ second. Fig. 39 explains the remaining step of the clock's operation.

The time is shown, without numerals, by the positions of hands, which are printed on each dial. The rate of flow of the water is 0.3 litres per minute or 100 drops per second and the total quantity of water used in the full closed circuit is approximately 8 litres.[227] The clock has a theoretical accuracy of 8 seconds in 24 hours.

The present clock offers a modern development of the control of a water-clock by a pendulum. Methods for doing this date back to the 17th century, the first apparently being that suggested by

227. D., 29.

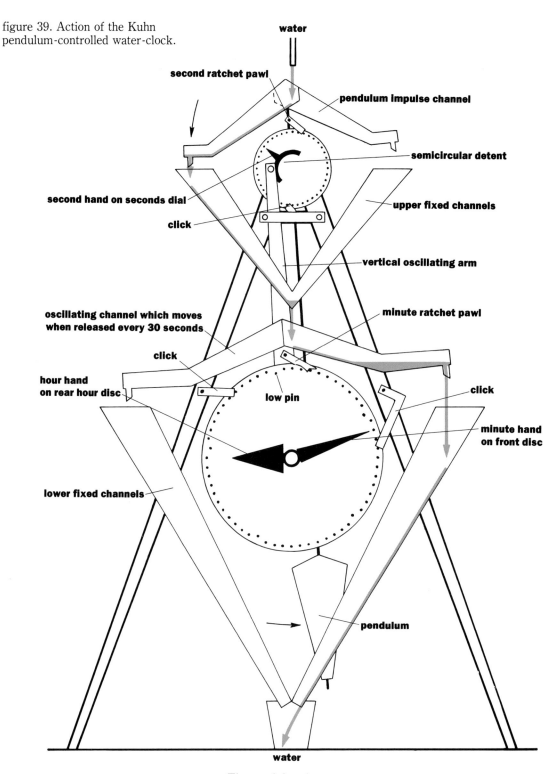

figure 39. Action of the Kuhn pendulum-controlled water-clock.

water

second ratchet pawl

pendulum impulse channel

semicircular detent

second hand on seconds dial

upper fixed channels

click

vertical oscillating arm

oscillating channel which moves when released every 30 seconds

minute ratchet pawl

click

hour hand on rear hour disc

low pin

click

minute hand on front disc

lower fixed channels

pendulum

water

a. The pendulum has swung to the right. The illustration shows the path of the water.

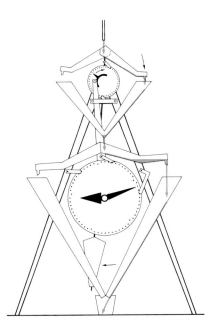

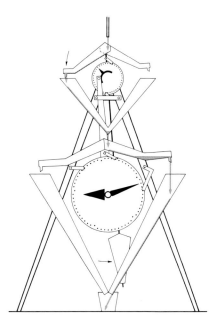

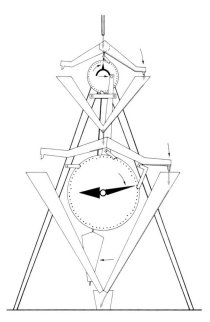

b. The pendulum swings to the left, operating the second ratchet pawl, which moves one pin of the second dial. Water meanwhile enters the top right pendulum impulse channel, providing impulse to the pendulum.

c. The pendulum swings to the right. The water enters the top left pendulum impulse channel, providing impulse to the pendulum and causing the second ratchet pawl to move back over a pin. This sequence repeats until the second hand gets to the top.

d. The pendulum swings to the left. The semicircular detent now allows the oscillating arm, under the weight of the water in the right oscillating channel, to swing to the right, thus operating the minute ratchet pawl, which moves a pin on the minute dial. The water then starts to fill the left oscillating channel.

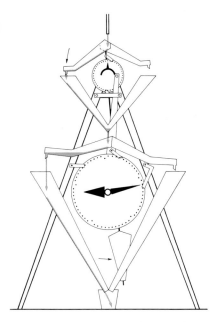

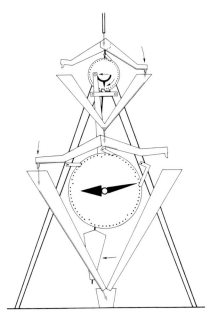

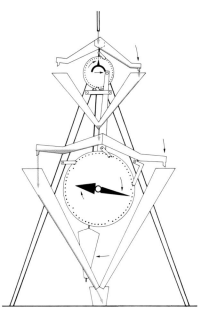

e. The pendulum then swings to the right. The left oscillating channel has by now filled with water but cannot move to the left because the oscillating arm is held by the semicircular detent. The sequence continues until the second hand is in the 30 seconds position.

f. The pendulum swings to the left. The second hand at bottom allows the semicircular detent to let the oscillating arm, under the weight of the water in the oscillating channel, move to the left, resetting the minute ratchet pawl. The sequence continues until the second hand is back at the top.

g. Every 12th pin on the minute wheel is lower than the others. When one of these low pins is in the top position, the minute ratchet pawl will engage the low pin, allowing the hour ratchet pawl to engage with a pin on the hour dial (behind the minute dial). At this time the seconds, minutes, and 1/5 hour are advanced.

figure 40. Perrault's escapement for a pendulum-controlled water-clock. From Gallon, i, pl. 1, no. 9.

Claude Perrault in a letter to Christiaan Huygens in 1669.[228] In this scheme the driving force was applied directly to the pendulum and did not pass through a train. Perrault further elaborated his idea and presented two memoirs on the subject to the Académie Royale des Sciences.[229] Kuhn's clock represents a further development of Perrault's principle. Presented as a decorative object for gardens, shops, offices, and the like, it was awarded a gold medal at the New York Exhibition, 1968,[230] and a silver medal at the Brussels Inventors' Fair of the same year.[231]

Provenance: Tiffany & Co., New York

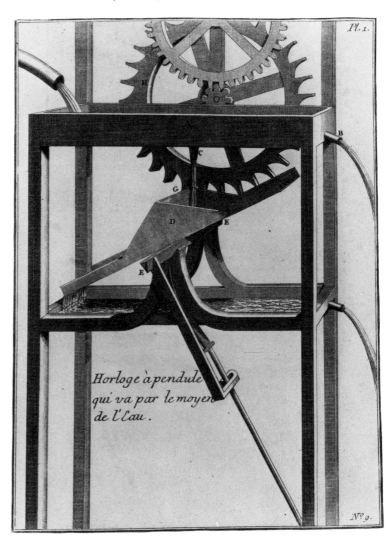

figure 41. Perrault's pendulum-controlled water-clock. From Gallon, i, pl. 2, no. 10

228. *Oeuvres complètes,* vi, The Hague, 1895, 506–12, reproducing Bibliothèque Nationale Ms Français 21259.
229. Gallon, 1, 39–43.
230. D., 29.
231. Information sheet (typescript) supplied with the clock (?) by H.A. Kuhn.

Sand-glasses

Sand-glasses

S and-glass is the generic name for an instrument that measures equal periods of time by the motion of a freely flowing powdered solid substance.[1] In form it comprises two equal-size triangular or conical bulbs or *ampoules* arranged mouth-to-mouth within a protective and supporting metal or wooden frame. No sand-glasses have survived from any period before the 16th century,[2] but there is ample literary, documentary, and iconographic evidence for their existence in 14th-and 15th-century Europe. From such sand-glasses as survive from the 16th century onwards, it has been possible to identify three main methods of manufacture:[3]

1. Up to approximately the second or third decades of the 18th

figure 42. A sand-glass maker's workshop. From Christoph Weigel, *Abbildung der Gemein-nutzlichen Haupstande*, Regensburg, 1698, 405.

1. Despite the fact that sand seems rarely to have been used in sand-glasses (see Drover *et al*), the name seems preferable to hourglass (the sand-glass seems seldom to have measured an hour) since it presumably tells us that sand was the substance originally used.
2. The earliest seems to be a remarkable glass now in the Department of Medieval and Later Antiquities, British Museum. It is in a painted stand and dated 1520.
3. By Hughes (I), 1622–3. His analysis is followed by Waters (II), 308–10, who provides additional detail.

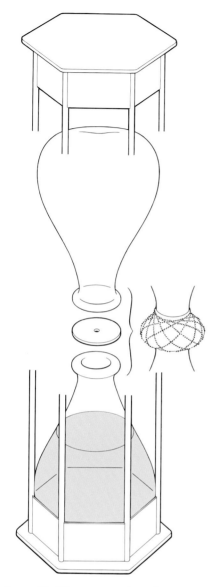

figure 43. The construction of sand-glasses.

figure 44 (opposite). Miniature from a German-Hebrew Pentateuch, Meghilloth, and Haphtaroth, A.D. 1395. British Library, London, Add Ms 19776 f. 72v.

century each of the two *ampoules* was blown separately, the ends of the neck being turned over and ground flat to form a flanged lip. A diaphragm of brass leaf was placed between the two flanges, and the joint was secured by pitch, wax, or putty bound over with canvas or another fabric and lashed tight with crisscrossed thread or gilt wire (fig. 43).

2. During the middle decades of the 18th century, a new technique was introduced. Although the *ampoules* were still blown separately, a drilled brass bead was placed between them and the glass itself fused round to form the joint.

3. From *c.* 1760/70 the two *ampoules* were blown as one piece, the sand being inserted afterwards through an opening in one end, which was then sealed with a cork covered in parchment or linen. Later this opening was itself filled with glass and ground smooth.

The period of time a sand-glass measures is an arbitrary one. It is decided by the whim of the maker or the task for which the glass is required, and may be for any interval from a few seconds up to 24 hours. Whatever the interval for which the sand-glass runs, however, the hours it measures are of equal duration, and will not, therefore, agree exactly with the hours measured by a sundial.

The earliest indisputable reference to a sand-glass so far found occurs among records of the English navy in 1345/6[4] when Thomas de Stetesham, clerk of the king's ship *La George* included among his receipts the entry '. . . paid at Lescluse [Sluys], in Flanders, for twelve glass horologes ("pro xii orologiis vitreis"), price of each 4½ gross,' in sterling 9s. Item, For four horologes of the same sort ("de eadem secta"), bought there, price of each five gross,' making in sterling *3s 4d.*' In 1380 'Ung grant orloge de mer, de deux grans fiolles plains de sablon, en ung grant estuy de boys garny d'archal' was listed among the effects of Charles V of France.[5] The earliest illustration also dates from the middle decades of the 14th century. It occurs in one of a series of frescoes by Ambrosio Lorenzetti in the Sala del Pace of the Palazzo Publico, Siena, depicting good and evil government and is used to symbolize temperance.[6] The only other known 14th-century illustration dates from 1395 and shows the instrument being used to time a schoolboy's lesson[7] (fig. 44).

Of the origins of the sand-glass and its development before 1300, however, nothing is known. Although its invention has variously been ascribed to classical antiquity; to a legendary monk named Liutprand of Chartres in the 8th century; and, with more plausibility,

4. 19 Edward III. See Nicolas, 476. I am grateful to Dr. J.B. Post of the Public Record Office for checking the date of this entry.
5. Labarte, 234.
6. Reproduced in Drover *et al*, figs. 1 & 2. Although the frescoes were executed in 1337–8, they were shortly afterwards damaged by fire. The area where the sand-glass is shown is unlikely to be earlier than the late 1350's. White (I) 192–3.
7. British Museum Add Ms 19776 f 72v, a German-Hebrew Pentateuch, Meghilloth, and Haphtaroth, A.D. 1395. For the illustration, see British Museum postcard OPB 6. For some discussion, with a reproduction, see Turner (II), 163.

בהבחיה ובמישרה אחזתנו לא ימכר ולא יגאל כל חרם קדש קדשים הוא ליהוה כל חרם אשר
יחרם מן האדם לא יפדה מות יומת וכל מעשר הארץ מזרע הארץ מפרי העץ ליהוה
הוא קדש ליהוה ואם גאל יגאל איש ממעשרו חמישיתו יסף עליו וכל מעשר בקר
וצאן כל אשר יעבר תחת השבט העשירי יהיה קדש ליהוה לא יבקר בין טוב לרע ולא
ימירנו ואם המר ימירנו והיה הוא ותמורתו יהיה קדש לא יגאל אלה המצות אשר
צוה יהוה את משה אל בני ישראל בהר סיני

סימן סכום פסוקי דספרא נטר לך

figure 45. Ship's glasses, *c.* 1735. Reproduced from Blanckley. *A Naval Expositor*, London, 1750. (Photograph: the British Library, London)

to the Mediterranean region, perhaps near Amalfi, in the 11th, 12th or 13th centuries, for navigational purposes, there is a total lack of evidence to support the first two suggestions, and only circumstantial and plausible arguments in favour of the third.[8] Although it is true that several of the early references to sand-glasses occur in a nautical context, this may be no more than a reflection of the biases of modern research. Certainly in the 14th and 15th centuries the sand-glass was a common object of daily life. At sea it would be used to measure out the period of the 'watch' (fig. 45), and perhaps as a navigational instrument in combination with the magnetic compass and portolan.[9]

Thanks to the realization that the word 'dyoll' found in English ship inventories of the 15th century should be interpreted as meaning sand-glass,[10] the naval area of use is by far the best documented. Measuring the period of a watch at sea, however, may be paralleled on land by the measuring of the length of a lesson in school or university, and of the intervals between the hours of prayer in monastic communities. A sand-glass, fulfilling this role as a scholar's timepiece, was frequently included in depictions of St. Jerome in his study.[11] Indeed it almost became the symbol of a learned man. Sand-glasses were sometimes shown furnished with a manual dial (usually divided in four-hour intervals), which may also be a simple scale of numbers, with an index, for counting the inversions of the glass, as on two examples now in the Mathematisch-Physikalischer Salon, Dresden.[12] The manual dial is attached to the top of the backboard if the sand-glass is mounted on a wall, or to one end of the instrument if it is shown carried by hand as in allegorical representations. In 1398 one Swiss town council ordered that the tolling of the bell for quarter- and half-hour periods was to be regulated by a sand-glass,[13] while a Parisian burgher's journal of a few years earlier (1392–94), by recording a recipe for sand-glass 'sand', shows that the object was also in domestic use.[14] Among other activities timed by sand-glasses in the 15th century we may mention the operation of a stamping mill,[15] and the length of jousts at the marriage of

8. For a general discussion of the problem of origins, see Turner (II).
9. Waters (I) *passim*.
10. Naish, 205–8. The crucial evidence is contained in a 15th-century set of sailing directions which describes the sea bottom in 15 fathoms off Penmark, Brittany, as 'Smale diale sonde,' i.e., fine sand suitable for sand-glasses. For an hypothesis concerning the origin of the word 'dyoll,' see Turner (II).
11. E.g. in depictions by Antonio del Fiore (1436), Petrus Christus (1442), G. Pencz (*c.* 1550), Albrecht Dürer (1511 & 1514). For the painting by Pencz, now in the Louvre, see Chapuis, 34; for the Dürer engravings, Knoppe, nos. 73 & 298.
12. Grötzsch, nos. 21 & 22. Manual dials for recording the passage of eight hours were still used in ships of the Royal Navy in the mid-18th century. See Blanckley (written 1732), 207. An example of such a dial is preserved in the National Maritime Museum, Greenwich.
13. Sternfeld, 12.
14. Power, 304.
15. Shown in an illustration to a manuscript *Feuerwerkbuch* (*c.* 1450), and reproduced in the Time Gallery, The Science Museum, London. For a similar illustration in the Hauslaub-Liechtenstein Ms "Das Fewrwerkpuch . . . alle die Stuck und Kunst die eine Jedlicher guter Puchsen Maister kinnen sol . . . ," *c.* 1450, see E. Weil, *Catalogue 16: Chemistry . . .* , n.d. [*c.* 1950] no. 93, outer back cover, and 18–19 for a description of the manuscript.

In the image: *Blasphemy. Rebellion. Heresie.* / *I know you are good fellows Stay and take the other glass.* / *No life to Lechery. Hugh Peters y first and y last.*

figure 46. A 17th-century pulpit-glass in use. Engraved frontispiece to W. Young, *England's Shame: or a Relation of the Life and Death of Hugh Peters,* London, 1663. Peters is shown in the act of turning the glass, making a poor pun while so doing.

Charles le Témeraire of Burgundy with Margaret of York in 1468.[16]

The role thus established for the sand-glass in medieval Europe was maintained in succeeding centuries. Despite the steady improvement of mechanical clocks and watches, and the proliferation of sundials, the sand-glass, possibly because it was much cheaper, retained its popularity and found new applications. Perhaps the most important of these was as a pulpit-glass in churches (fig. 46)

16. Vivielle, 11, presumably recalling the *Memoirs* of Olivier de la Marche. Sternfeld, 8, dates the episode incorrectly in 1475.

where, as the sermon was increasingly emphasized in the 16th and 17th centuries, some device was wanted that 'the preacher might know how the hour passed away,'[17] and the congregation how long he had preached.[18] The glass was usually attached to the pulpit by a metal bracket (the 'cadge' or carrier), which was often decorative and occasionally elaborate.[19] As an emblem of mortality, sand-glasses were sometimes incorporated in the funeral garlands hung in churches to celebrate the death of a virgin,[20] and there must have been numerous other particular uses which have now been forgotten. In 1716, for example, Francis Place, describing the working methods of the great *emigré* engraver Wenceslaus Hollar (1607–1677) some decades earlier, remarked that 'he had a method of working not common. He did all by the hour, in which he was very exact, for if anybody came in, and kept him from his business, he always laid the hour-glass on one side, till they were gone.'[21] Bidding to purchase the profits of tollgates in the 18th century was timed against a one-minute sand-glass,[22] and three-minute glasses were incorporated into late-Georgian egg-boilers, cumbersome devices intended to prepare breakfast eggs on the table.[23] The three-minute egg-timer is of course still with us. Twenty-eight and sixty-six second log-glasses remained part of the standard ship issue in the Royal Navy until 1839. Even in the 20th century (until 1951), the ringing of the division bells in the House of Commons of the British Parliament was timed by a two-minute sand-glass.

Most familiar in a domestic context, the sand-glass also played a part in scientific work. Of its role in navigation something has already been said.[24] It was also particularly suitable for use by astronomers, thanks to its quality of measuring equal hours. Efforts were made to refine its accuracy in the 16th and 17th centuries, as rapid advances in astronomical theory and observational accuracy made the problem of precise timekeeping ever more acute. Thus the Danish observer Tycho Brahe (1546–1601) in his constant search for an accurate timekeeper experimented with a glass of 24-hours' duration, graduated into hours and minutes and filled with calcinated lead.[25] Similarly, sand-glasses were included among the observatory equipment of Tycho's Turkish contemporary Taqi ad Din

figure 47. Allegory of Death (marble statue), from the Charnier des Innocents, Paris, *c.* 1530. Musée des Arts Decoratifs, Paris. figure 48 (opposite). Allegory of Death. Detail.

17. Expenses of St. Catherines, City of London, which in 1564 spent 12d on an hourglass for this reason. Cited from Hughes (I) 1623.
18. For some amusing anecdotes about sandglasses and the length of sermons, see Fairholt, Chambers, ii, 712–4.
19. Although once common, pulpit-glasses surviving *in situ* are now rare. A number of examples, however, are discussed and illustrated by Fairholt, Chambers, and Cumming. The fullest survey of them, however, with a checklist of then-surviving examples, is to be found in Cox, 147–62.
20. Chambers, i, 271–4.
21. Cited from Hind, 5.
22. Searle, ii, 5.
23. Hughes (II) 1334–5.
24. For further details, see Sternfeld, 15–18; Waters (II), 309–10. For an excellent, clear, contemporary account of the problems of timekeeping and the sand-glass at sea, see Polter, sigs. E1v-E4v. For Columbus' use of sand-glasses, Heers, 311–2.
25. Sternfeld, 13.

Muḥammad b. ar-Rashīda b. Maʿrūf b. Aḥmad, the chief astronomer at Istanbul from A.H. 979 [A.D. 1571/2].[26] The search by Renaissance horologists for a more constant force than that provided by a falling weight regulated by an escapement also led attention to the sand-glass. In 1665 Archangelo Maria Radi suggested using either twelve sand-glasses inside a weight-driven wheel or a compartmented cylinder with sand dropping through holes in the divisions as a means of controlling a complex geared bell-ringing device.[27] Other attempts to develop the sand-glass were described by Domenico Martinelli.[28] In 1684, Philipe de la Hire published a description of a new form of sand-glass for marine use. Shaped like an inverted thermometer with a single tube, the sand in the bulb at the top measured thirty minutes against a scale on the column, after which it was reversed and the time read off a second scale as it returned down the column.[29] In 1724 the Chevalier d'Albert described to the Académie Royale his solution to the problem of determining longitude by local differences in the time of sunset. These he wished to measure by a sand-glass, the *ampoules* being formed as a straight cylinder tapering in a cone and having a glass diaphragm.[30] Three years later Comte Prosper described to the same body an 'horloge à sable' to measure the lengths of time by the weight of sand fallen into a narrow cylindrical column from a reservoir above.[31] Use of the sand-glass at sea was the prize subject propounded by the Académie Royale in 1725, the award going to Daniel Bernouilli (1700–1781),[32] and several unsolicited suggestions on this subject were received by the English Board of Longitude in the 18th and early 19th centuries.[33] An interesting development, registered by Gray and Keen of Liverpool, 1 October 1849, was the 'Aural log timer' in which two cylinders of metal tapered to a narrow aperture at one end, were joined together in the manner of a sand-glass, and filled with lead shot. The noise of the lead shot falling onto the lower

26. Two sand-glasses are shown in the well-known illustration of Taqī ad-Dīn's observatory in the Shāhinshāh-nāma (History of the King of Kings), an epic poem celebrating Sultan Murād III of Turkey (reigned A.H. 982–1003 [A.D. 1574–95]), by ʿAlā ad-Dīn Mansūr-i Shīrazī, Istanbul University Library, Ms. Yildiz 2652/260 (=F.14104), f57r. It is reproduced in colour in Nasr, 113 and outer back jacket. That large sandglasses were familiar in 16th-century Turkey is suggested by Dominico Yerushalmi's description of *horologgi da Polvere*, sand-glasses 'which are so large that they run the whole day without needing constant turning over.' Cited from Kurz, 45, no. 1, who, however, thinks that what Yerushalmi saw must have been a clepsydra using sand instead of water.

27. *Nuova Scienza di Horologi a polvere che mostrano e' suonano distintamente tuute l'Hore*, 1665. Often cited as the only book on sand-glasses, this short pamphlet is not concerned at all with sand-glasses as such, but with a form of sand-clock.

28. *Horologi elementari, divisi in quattro parti. Nella prima parte fatti con l'acqua. Nella seconda con la terra. Nella terza con l'aria. Nella quarta col fuoco. Alcuni muti, & alcuni suono. Tutti facili, e molto commodi*, Venice, 1669, part II. This is partly based on Radi's work.

29. *Journal des Scavans*, 1684, 368 & 270. Summarized in Baillie, 112.

30. Le Chevalier d'Albert, 'Methode pour trouver les Longitudes' in Gallon, iv, 89–91.

31. *Ibid.*, v, 23–9.

32. Baillie, 164.

33. For example by William Butler, 'About a 24 hour glass' Bd. of Longitude Papers, 1785, vol. xxxiii(i) 5, 21–9; by John Patteshall, 'A Mercurial Hour-Glass,' 1786, vol. xxxiii (ii) 31, 265–71; by Q. Adams, 'Finding Longitude by a Sand-glass,' 1800, vol. xxx (1) 1, 3–8; and by W. Adams 'On the sand glass as a means of ascertaining the time at Sea,' 1810. vol. xxix, 19, 253–6.

figure 49. A self-turning sand-glass by
Grollier de Servière (petit fils).

cylinder gave aural indication of the time to the linesman.[34] It had a
duration of 14 seconds.

Attention, however, was not entirely concentrated on the sea.
Particularly important and successful was the development of a very
small glass for use by physicians when timing the beat of a patient's
pulse,[35] a usage which sustained itself well into the 19th century. Attempts were also made to render the ordinary domestic glass more
commodious. Thus at least three mechanisms to turn the glass automatically when it was empty were developed independently during

34. A surviving example (serial no. 2013) now in the Mariner's Museum, Newport News,
Virginia, is described and illustrated by Calhoun, 9–11.
35. A pulse glass of 25-seconds' duration, which once belonged to the celebrated physician
John Coakley Lettsom (1744–1815), is preserved in the Museum of the History of Science, Oxford. For a description, see Turner (I), 88, & illus. on 59.

the later 17th century, some of them published[36] (fig. 49). In 1746 the Abbé Soumille presented a sand-glass with a dial to show the hours and minutes to the Académie Royale des Sciences, Paris.[37]

At least from the 16th century, sand-glasses had been made in sets of two, three, or four glasses within a single frame (catalogue nos. 10–12), the separate glasses usually measuring different periods of time.[38] In a variant of this, particularly popular in 18th-century France, a single glass was blown with three or four *ampoules* instead of two, thus enabling the quarters to be read off more easily as the sand fell (catalogue nos. 16 & 17). Other attempts at improvement had concentrated on the filling used in the glasses. That considerable care and attention had to be paid to the preparation of the 'sand' was early recognized. It is shown by the detailed instructions given by the Goodman of Paris,[39] whose 'sand' was marble sawdust. In the following centuries a wide variety of fillings were tried for sand-glasses. They included fine-sieved and cleaned sea or river sand, lead or tin dust, marble powder, and pulverized eggshell. For the latter there is some slight evidence to suggest that it was fairly generally used in the later 17th and 18th centuries.[40] Only in the 20th century has a more convenient substance been found in the form of extremely small glass globules of uniform size.[41]

Attribution and Dating

Very few sand-glasses are signed or dated. In the present catalogue, attributions and dates are suggested tentatively on stylistic grounds following a survey of dated illustrations of sand-glasses in European paintings.

36. By C.D.O., *Journal des Scavans*, 1682, Baillie, 111. The glass turned every 30 minutes, and operated for 30 hours. By Grollier de Servière (petit fils), *Receuil d'Ouvrages Curieux de Mathématiques et de Méchaniques où Description du Cabinet de Monsieur Grollier de Servière*, Lyon, 1719, who supported the sand-glass on an axis and arranged a false bottom to the ampoules. When all the sand had run into one *ampoule*, the false flexible bottom stretched under the weight of the sand below the level of the base where it pressed on a counterweight, which in turn released the detent of a spring which turned the axis and the glass attached to it. By Stefan Farfler in 1655, for whom see Lunardi, 72.

37. Baillie, 223.

38. Probably just such a set were the 'Four hour-glasses set in ebony, in a box of printed leather' listed in 1553 in the account of Sir Andrew Dudley and Arthur Storton, Keeper of the Palace at Westminster. *HMC Hatfield House Mss* I, 128.

39. Above, n. 14.

40. For a detailed account of fillings, see Drover *et al*.

41. Cassidy. Cited from Drover *et al*, vi, n.13.

Sand-glasses
Catalogue

8. German Wall Sand-glass

17th century
Iron, painted red with traces of yellow, and glass
Width across top bar 8¾ in. (222 mm)
Not signed
Inventory 343

A horizontal bar is surmounted by a coat of arms now indistinguishable and with the crest of an eagle with spread wings facing right. Attached to the underside of the bar are two vertical struts to which two rectangular brackets are pivoted (one at each end). Their free ends are attached through a rivet to one end of the sand-glass holder. The glass hangs vertically from one of these brackets at one end of the mount. When the sand has run completely through, and the glass requires turning, it is only necessary to push the glass to an horizontal position when its own weight will cause the empty part to fall, thus leaving the sand-glass suspended from the second bracket and inverted from its previous position (fig. 50). The sand-glass mount has four

figure 50. Catalogue no. 8.
Diagram of the action.

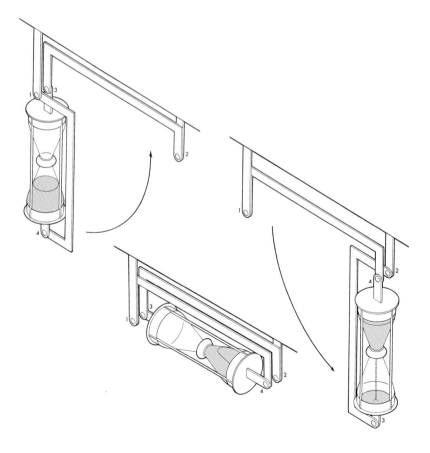

figure 51. Catalogue no. 8:
German wall sand-glass.

figure 52. Catalogue no. 8.
Partly dismantled.

turned pillars. The shaped *ampoules* were blown separately, and have a brass diaphragm sealed into the joint, which is bound round with red silk and brass-covered twine. The filling is white 'sand.' Duration: approximately 30 minutes.

This well-made sand-glass has an unusual mounting for which a parallel is provided by four other examples. These are:

1. A finely made silver-gilt example with chased and moulded foliate and grotesque mask decoration on the pillars, and scrolled dolphins on either side of a winged cherub's head on the pediment. Not signed or dated. Slightly bulbous glasses. Museum of Fine Arts, Boston (Theodore Wilbur Fund in memory of Charlotte Beebe Wilbur), inventory number 57. 533.[42] Ascribed to the second or third quarter of the 16th century.

2. Painted iron with turned pillars and upper edges of bars scalloped. Surmounted by a central tree with two smaller trees or bushes on either side, and on one side a prancing stag. 17th century. Victoria & Albert Museum, London.[43]

3. As 2, but with larger central tree and with a prancing (?) horse rather than a stag. Slightly more tapering *ampoules* than the other examples. Austrian Museum for Applied Arts, Vienna.[44]

4. Painted iron, similar scalloped decoration as 2 and 3 but surmounted by Adam and Eve on either side of the Tree of Knowledge round the trunk of which twines the serpent offering Eve an apple. Deutsches Museum, Munich.[45]

Of these, 2, 3, 4, and the present example show close stylistic similarities and may be ascribed to the same *atelier.* This was probably, but not certainly, German.

Provenance: From the village of Knöplen, Switzerland.

42. See *Apollo,* January, 1970, 74; Ramsey; Vincent.
43. Illustrated in Harford, 164.
44. Illustrated in Basserman-Jordan, 233 and dated *c.* 1725. This example was previously in the Figdor and d'Allemagne collections. See d'Allemagne, 178, where the device is ascribed to upper Bavaria and dated 16th century.
45. Illustrated in Lubke, fig. 138, 92, and dated 1550.

9. Sand-glass of Unknown Origin

17th century
Oak and glass
Overall height 22⅜ in. (568 mm)
Not signed
Inventory 494

The instrument has a circular stand with three turned columns. The *ampoules* are straight-sided, and taper sharply for about three-quarters of their depth. They are separately blown, and joined at the centre by a painted brass sleeve. The filling is red 'sand.' Duration: 24 hours.

figure 53. Catalogue no. 9:
Sand-glass of unknown origin.

10. German Sand-glass Set

17th century
Beaten brass and glass
Frame 9⁷/₈ in. × 2¹/₂ in. (251 mm × 63 mm)
Overall height of mount 19 in. (482 mm)
Not signed
Inventory 1546

On the beaten rectangular stand are barley-twist pillars (one missing and one replaced). There are four glasses for fifteen, thirty, forty-five, and sixty minutes, the durations being painted on the *ampoules*, although they are now much worn, as ¹/₄, ²/₄, ³/₄, and ⁴/₄. The flanged joints are sealed with wax or putty bound over with fabric and lashed with thread. At a later date (? in the 19th century), the central front pillar was removed and the central back strip replaced. A crudely decorated ornately shaped strip punched with the initials M G and the date 1625 was then soldered to the frame and a central pivot bolted into place with a heavy nut. To this pivot was bolted an arm carrying an ornate beaten backpiece depicting a bust of a figure in Roman dress with a laurel wreath, mounted on a pedestal flanked by military emblems and surrounded with volute and acanthus-leaf decoration. This backpiece being hung on a wall, the sand-glass set could be turned on the pivot at the end of each hour. White 'sand' filling. Published: UTO, lot 177a.

figure 54. Catalogue no. 10:
German sand-glass set.

11. German Sand-glass Set

Late 17th century
Oak painted black, and glass
9½ in. × 5⅝ in. × 3 in. (242 mm × 143 mm × 76 mm)
Not signed
Inventory 116

This two-glass wall set has five pillars of which the front three have simple carved decoration. There is an ogee-arched frieze to both top and bottom of the stand. The straight, slightly convex, conical *ampoules* are separately blown. The joints are sealed with wax or mastic, bound round with leather, and lashed with twine. The filling is white 'sand.' Duration: 30 and 60 minutes.

This example should be compared with the sand-glass set with two glasses shown at the right-hand side of the workman's bench in fig. 42, which it resembles both in the shape of the *ampoules* and in the ogival decoration.

figure 55. Catalogue no. 11: German sand-glass set.

12. German Sand-glass Set

Early 18th century
Brass, iron, and glass
9¾ in. × 11¼ in. × 2 in.
(248 mm × 286 mm × 51 mm)
Not signed
Inventory 79

figure 56. Catalogue no. 12. Detail.
figure 57 (below). Catalogue no. 12.
Back view.

The four-glass set is contained in a shaped brass stand with seven scroll pillars. The eighth pillar appears to have been replaced by a metal strip and a funnel carried from its centre point to the pillar immediately in front. Through this funnel or sleeve passes an iron axle with a handle at one end (cast in one piece with the axle) and a screw thread at the other, which carries a six-point (creator's) star at the front. This acts as a nut. Attached to this axle is a vertical bar with supporting bracket ending in a bolt for hanging the set from a ceiling or other horizontal surface. Also carried on this vertical bar is a hooped spring, the ends of which press on each side of the axle, thus ensuring that the stand is properly set in the vertical position when it is turned. The *ampoules* are straight, flaring outwards and are separately blown. The flanged joints with brass diaphragms are bound over with yellow velvet and copper-covered twine. White 'sand' filling with varying degrees of fineness. Duration: 15, 30, 45, and 60 minutes.

figure 58. Catalogue no. 12:
German wall sand-glass set.

13. French Sand-glass

Mid-18th century
Brass and glass
Height 17⅞ in. (454 mm)
Not signed
Inventory 1176

An octagonal base has eight struts and two suspension rings. The glass is blown in two parts secured at the joint (probably with a flange) by wax, bound over with velvet, and crossed with thread. One large *ampoule* is formed in the usual manner. The other *ampoule* is formed in six almost-spherical, interconnecting sections.

When the 'sand' is in the larger *ampoule* and the larger *ampoule* is on top, the 'sand' falls into the sectioned *ampoule*, filling up the bottommost spherical section first, at which point ten minutes have elapsed. In like manner, the other five sections are filled in turn, enabling the user to observe the passing of each ten-minute period of the hour. When the glass is turned over, the sectioned *ampoule* is on top. The 'sand' falls, emptying the topmost spherical section first, again indicating the passage of ten minutes. The remaining five sections are emptied similarly. Orange 'sand' filling. Duration: 60 minutes.

figure 59. Catalogue no. 13:
French sand-glass.

14. Sand-glass of Unknown Origin

? Mid-18th century
Wood, covered with leather and fish-skin, and glass
Height 3½ in. (89 mm)
Diameter 1¼ in. (32 mm)
Not signed
Inventory 1643

The double *ampoule* glass was probably flanged at the centre with a brass diaphragm. The joint is sealed with wax or putty bound over with canvas and lashed with copper-covered twine. It is contained in a double case with cutaway sides, the outer case being rotatable so that the instrument is fully enclosed when not in use. This characteristic has led to the assumption that glasses of this kind were intended for voyages and travel. The black 'sand' filling is probably composed of iron filings. Duration: 30 minutes.

The origin of glasses of this type is not known, but they perhaps date to the 16th century, when Martin Luther is supposed to have possessed such a sand-glass.[46] A leather-cased example in the Uhrenmuseum, Wuppertal, has been ascribed to the 15th century[47] although there is no obvious evidence to support the conjecture. Fourteen- and twenty-eight-second log glasses of the 18th and 19th century were made in this form,[48] and a similar type is shown in Weigel's illustration of a sand-glass maker's shop (fig. 42).

46. Junger, 191. See also Cumming, fig. 5.
47. Aked, fig. 5.
48. Hill & Paget-Tomlinson, 56.

figure 60 (far left). Catalogue
no. 14. Outer case.
figure 61 (left). Catalogue no. 14.
Inner case with glass.
figure 62 (right). Catalogue no.
14: Sand-glass of unknown
origin. Fully assembled.

15. French Sand-glass

Mid-18th cenury
Brass and glass
Overall height 6¹/₈ in. (155 mm)
Not signed
Inventory 1531

The sexagonal base has six pillars and a perforated frieze. The two *ampoules* are flanged at the joint, which is covered with green cloth and lashed with twine. One *ampoule* is formed in the usual manner. The other *ampoule* consists of two interconnecting sections, thus enabling the quarter-hours to be read. The manner of operation is similar to that described in catalogue entry number 13. Light brown 'sand' filling. Duration: 30 minutes.

figure 63. Catalogue no. 15:
French sand-glass.

16. French Multiple Sand-glass

18th century
Brass and glass
Height 9⅛ in. (232 mm)
Not signed
Inventory 115

Six pillars are on the sexagonal stand. The instrument has one large *ampoule*, and another is blown in four sections to indicate the quarter-hours. The manner of operation is similar to that found in the commentary to catalogue entry number 13. The joint has a brass diaphragm, sealed beneath green velvet and bound with silver-covered twine. White 'sand' filling. Duration: 60 minutes.

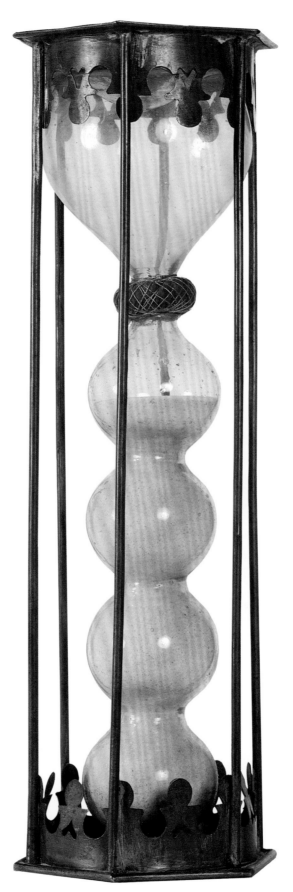

figure 64. Catalogue no. 16:
French multiple sand-glass.

17. French or Italian Multiple Sand-glass

18th century
Pasteboard, with straw inlay worked in
formal semi-geometric patterns in scarlet,
green, and gold; inside of stand
lined with an embossed paper; and glass
Height 10½ in. (267 mm)
Not signed
Inventory 481

The multiple glass has one conventional *ampoule* at one end. The second *ampoule*, at the other end, was blown in four sections to indicate the quarter-hours. The operation is similar to that described in catalogue entry 13. The joint is bound round with canvas and gold wire. Light brown 'sand' filling. Duration: 60 minutes.

Provenance: Marouf, Sale III, 27 March 1971, Lot 66, pl. 13.

figure 65. Catalogue no. 17:
French or Italian sand-glass.

18. English or German Sand-glass

Last quarter of 18th century
Brass and glass
Height 4¾ in. (121 mm)
Not signed
Inventory 31

A double *ampoule* is fused at the centre with a brass diaphragm. The joint is cemented with wax or putty covered with green velvet and bound with copper-covered twine. The glass is contained in a double brass case with cutaway sides. The outer case may be rotated to close the aperture, thus protecting the *ampoules* when the instrument is not in use. For this reason such glasses have been commonly assumed to have been used primarily by travellers.[49] Pink 'sand' filling. Duration: 30 minutes.

49. See commentary to cat. no. 14.

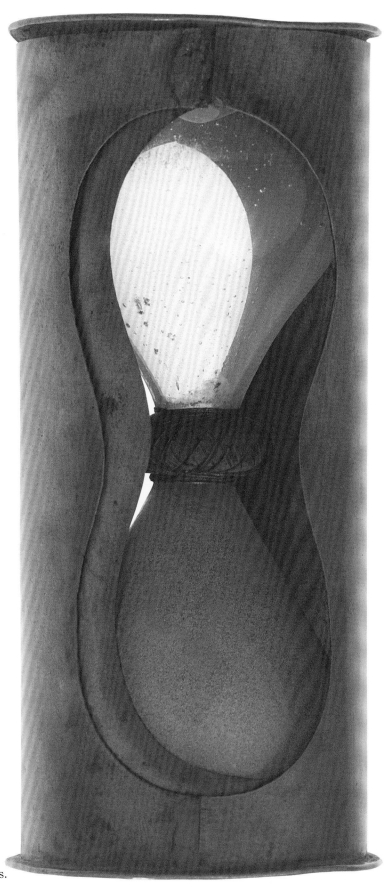

figure 66. Catalogue no. 18:
English or German sand-glass.

19. English Sand-glass

18th century
Soft wood stand painted red, glass ampoules
in leather mounts
Height 10½ in. (257 mm)
Not signed
Inventory 439

Four shaped pillars contain the *ampoules*. The joint is sealed with mastic bound over with twine. This is an extremely plain example, which is possibly a ship's glass. It should be compared with the examples shown (fig. 45) by Thomas Blanckley in his *A Naval Expositor*, 1750, written in 1732. The filling is light-beige 'sand.' Duration: 2 minutes, 40 seconds.

figure 67. Catalogue
no. 19: English sand-glass.

20. French Sand-glass

18th century
Mahogany and glass
Height 4⅝ in. (117 mm)
Not signed
Inventory SGA 1

The stand has four shaped pillars. The glass *ampoules* are blown in one piece with the neck formed in the glass. A hole at the end of one of the *ampoules* was used for filling the glass, and this has been plugged with a leather-covered stopper. The glass could be timed exactly by adding or removing 'sand.' This glass was possibly for nautical use. Light brown and black 'sand' filling. Duration: 28 seconds.

figure 68.
Catalogue no. 20:
French sand-glass.

Fire-clocks

Fire Clocks

A mong the most primitive, although probably not the oldest, of time measurers are devices which utilize the regular consumption of a combustible substance such as oil, wax, or incense. For convenience such devices are discussed here under two heads:

1. Devices employing the principles of candles and lamps.
2. Devices using incense.

Candle- and Lamp-clocks

Use of the regular burning of a protected candle to measure the passing of time was apparently widespread in both Oriental and Occidental societies during the medieval period. The earliest reference to the practice so far discovered occurs in China in a poem by You Jiangu (*fl. c.* A.D. 520). Here apparently the graduated candle supplied a means of determining time at night, the equivalent function during the day being performed by the burning of incense. Similar candles were also used in Japan until the early 10th century A.D.[1] Better known is the candle time-measurer, the invention of which is traditionally ascribed to Alfred the Great *c.* 878. Alfred's device consisted of six candles made from seventy-two pennyweights of wax, each being twelve inches high, of uniform thickness, and divided into twelve sections each of one inch. Since each candle burned away completely in four hours, each graduation measured twenty minutes. The candles were placed for protection inside cases made of a wooden frame with transparent horn panels in the sides.[2] The device no doubt worked, albeit somewhat murkily. Although we may reasonably doubt that it was really invented by King Alfred, there seems no reason to think that such candles were not used at his and other courts in Western Europe. Similar methods of measuring time were used in medieval churches, first by simply counting the number of candles of a specific size burnt, later by use of a graduated candle.[3] To regulate the time he could spend in bible reading and meditation, Louis IX of France (1214–1270) had three-foot graduated candles made and, according to Christine de Pisan, the method was still used by Charles V (1337–1380), who had a 'burning candle which was divided into twenty-four parts, in his chapel.'[4]

1. Bedini (II), 6 & 27.
2. *Eulogium Historiarum,* A.D. 878; Asser's *Life of Alfred,* c. 104. Below, cat. no. 21.
3. Havard, 57–64.
4. Solente, i, ch. xvi.

figure 69 (opposite). Candle-clock of the swordsman. From a manuscript of al-Jazarī copied in A.H. 715 (A.D. 1315/16). (Courtesy of the Freer Gallery of Art, Smithsonian Institution, Washington, D.C.)

figure 70. Candle-clock. From the *Libros del Saber . . .* , *c.* 1276. After Rico y Sinobas.

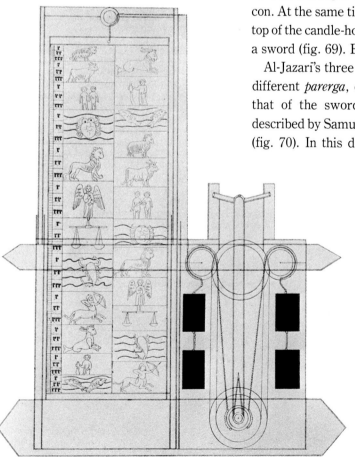

That the graduated candle was widely known and used in the Middle Ages seems also to be implied by the fact that it was developed. In his great treatise on mechanical devices completed in A.D. 1206, al-Jazarī described four forms of candle-clock which he had devised. Although he says that he has never seen such a thing, or any treatises concerning them, he does remark that, 'I heard tell, however, of a candle-holder with a brass candlestick on it in which was a wax candle whose wick went through a hole in a cross-piece at the top of the brass candlestick. Near the foot of the candlestick was the head of a lion. When a constant hour had passed from the lighting of the candle a ball fell from the mouth of the lion onto the bottom of the candle-holder.'[5] Further on he adds that he had examined a candle timepiece by Yūnus al-Asturlābī which did not work, '. . . the design was useless, its failure being due to the overflow of the wax.'[6] Evidently, therefore, by the mid-12th century in Islam, there was already some limited tradition of applying candles to time measurement, and this al-Jazarī considerably advanced. Basically he carried his candle inside a holder on a platform, which, by means of a rope, weight, and pulley system, automatically thrust the candle upwards each hour as it burnt away. Set down the side of the candle-holder was a channel containing fourteen balls. As the bottom of the candle lifted, it allowed one ball to fall from the channel into a trough, whence it disgorged through the mouth of a falcon. At the same time it actuated the arm of a slave seated near the top of the candle-holder who cut off the burnt part of the candle with a sword (fig. 69). Each hour the cycle repeated.[7]

Al-Jazarī's three other designs for candle-clocks, although using different *parerga*, depended basically upon the same principle as that of the swordsman. Quite different was the candle-clock described by Samuel el-Levi of Toledo in the *Libros del Saber* of 1276 (fig. 70). In this device there were neither automata figures nor

5. Hill (I) 83.
6. *Ibid.*, 87. In his commentary (272), Hill suggests that Yūnus al-Asṭurlābī is perhaps to be identified with the astronomer Ibn Yūnus aṣ-Ṣafadī (d. A.H. 399 [A.D. 1008/9]). Perhaps a more likely identification is with Yūnus b. al-Husayn al-Asṭurlābī, who signed a surviving brass globe in A.H. 539 [A.D. 1144/5]. See Destombes, Mayer (II), 296; Brieux & Maddison.
7. Hill (I), 83–7.

منصلان بهاطوبان
على بكتين زعليها
ت طرفاهامنصلا
بالنقالة ومتى اشتعلت
الشمعة اول الليل
فان الشمع تذهبه
النار فترتفع الشمعة
بجذب النقالة لها
حتى ترتفع الكفة
عن بندقة واحدة
والماضى من الليل
ساعة مستوية فيقع
البندقة الى الكفة آ
المتصلة بخيط س
وهو المتصل بفاصل
يد الغلام وعليه
م فينزل البندقة
فى الكفة حتى
يجلس الكفة على
ارض حن ويدحرج
وتخرج الى راس

aural time signals, only a visual indication from a series of tablets that rose as the candle burned, being actuated by a weight-and-pulley drive.[8] Although Samuel el-Levi's device bears some relationship with the Islamic tradition, like the mercury clock of Ishāq b. Sīd in the same collection, its immediate antecedents are unknown, and it has no known successors. That candle-clocks continued in use, however, is clear from the evidence already cited; apparently they also continued to be used in China, at least in the temples, for between A.D. 1330 and 1333, the discrepancy between solar time measured by a sundial and mean time measured by a candle seems to have been noticed by Fan Shunquian.[9]

After the end of the 14th century we have little information about time-measuring candles and it is possible with the rapid development of the mechanical clock in the late 13th and early 14th centuries, and of new forms of portable sundials in the 14th and 15th centuries, that they fell rather rapidly out of use. The curiosity of Renaissance *savants*, however, led to the development of a new kind of instrument.

In 1550, Girolamo Cardano included a description of the fountain feed lamp in his work *de Subtilitate* and although there is no need to consider him the inventor, the device probably came into general use at about this time.[10] Soon after, lamps of this sort were adapted to measure time by having the reservoir blown in glass and engraving on it a series of uniformly spaced hour lines. The time could be read off by noting the level of the oil against this scale. Time lamps of this kind are familiar from the 18th and 19th centuries, but there is no precise information available about their origins. Perhaps this should be sought in the 16th century when there was investigation of the subject. In October 1567, Joachim Hopper wrote to the Dutch statesman Viglius van Aytta van Zuchem (1507–1577) about the condition of a learned expatriate from Louvain, Hugo Helt (*c.* 1525–1594/5). Among other things Hopper remarked that Helt had spent twelve years developing a self-filling oil lamp that indicated the time.[11] Helt by this time had lived in Spain for at least twenty-two years, partly at Salamanca, and partly at or near Madrid.[12] At the latter city he may have been acquainted with a fellow Netherlander, Jehan l'Hermite (1560–1622) from Antwerp, who was a gentleman of the chamber to Phillip II. L'Hermite recorded that among the contents of his master's room was a timekeeper which showed the hours at night.[13] This, however, was an illuminated

8. Rico, iv, 77–93. The device is summarized by Bedini (III). A full translation, with commentary, of the Castilian text is being prepared by Dr. D.R. Hill, Great Bookham, England.
9. Needham & Wang Ling (I), 331.
10. Bedini (III), 31–2. That there may have been some investigation of lamp timekeepers in early Islam is, however, suggested by the Banū Mūsà's remark that a lamp with a self-feeding wick may be adopted to show the passage of time. Hill (IV), 237.
11. Maddison, 59.
12. *Ibid.,* 58–9.
13. Ruelens (II), 173–6.

spring-driven monstrance clock. That Helt's lamp clock was something similar, or resembled the familiar Dutch lamp timekeeper of later years, we can only speculate.

There were, after all, other possibilities. In 1663 the Jesuit Pierre Bobynet described three forms of oil-lamp clock in his treatise on dialling.[14] One of these was of the familiar form with glass reservoir. In the same work he described two forms of candle-clock[15] (fig. 73). Five years later Martinelli described a lamp which drove the wheel-work of a conventional looking clock on the principle of a smoke-jack[16] (fig. 71). A similar device was included among the 'other curious pieces . . .' that accompanied Mrs. Salmon's famous London exhibition of wax works in the late 17th century.[17] In 1696, Venturus

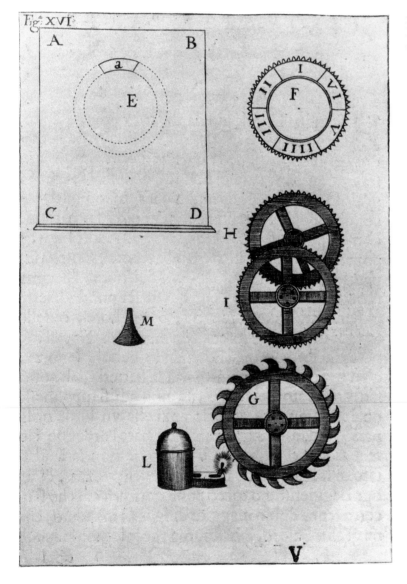

figure 71. Fire-clock. From Domenico Martinelli, *Horologi elementari, divisi in quattro parti*, Venice, 1669.

14. Bobynet, 303–8, and pl. 21.
15. *Ibid.*, 308–10, and cat. no. 22.
16. Martinelli, fig. xvi.
17. Advertisement in the Bagford collection, British Museum Harleian Manuscript 5931, reprinted in Wood, 100–1.

Mandey and Joseph Moxon,[18] deriving the idea from Francesco de Lana,[19] described an oil lamp with a dial and hand driven by a cord attached to a float in the oil reservoir. The cord ran over a pulley and was counterweighted to turn the index arbor as the oil level sank.

In 1730 and succeeding years, a flurry of advertisements by John Walker and Leonard Ashburne in *The Country Gentleman or the Craftsman*, in *The Daily Post*, and in *The Gentleman's Magazine* provide the first documentary evidence for the familiar oil lamp timepiece (fig. 75).[20] Walker's lamp was made of pewter and had a tall cylindrical reservoir clearly engraved with the hour numerals.[21] Thereafter examples of the lamp timekeeper have survived in plenty, although a number with small bulbous reservoirs cannot have worked with any great accuracy. The late 18th and 19th centuries saw many refinements essayed of which the most amusing was perhaps that of Hisashige Tanaka in 1837,[22] while others adapting the time measurer to new forms and styles of lamp somewhat improved its performance. In this context the lamp clocks of W.H. & S. Jackson, Gabry de Liancourt, Victor Athanase Pierret, Weaver, and Grand-Vals may be mentioned,[23] while the popularity of the form is attested by the filing of fifteen British patents on the subject between 1855 and 1900.

18. *Mechanick-Powers: or the Mystery of Nature and Art Unvail'd,* London, 1696.
19. *Magisterum naturae et artis opus Physico-Mathematicum P. Francesco Tertii de Lanis Societatis Iesu. Brixiensis in quo occultora naturalis Philosophiae Principia manefestante et multiplicum experimentum . . . ,* Brescia, 1684, pl. xviii. A later edition was published at Parma in 1692.
20. See Wood, 128–30 and Bedini (IV) 33–4.
21. See an example now in the Whipple Museum of the History of Science.
22. le Locle, no. 206, 31–2.
23. All these are described by Bedini (IV), 34–8. An example of Gabry de Liancourt's type made by 'Romuald Bozek in Prag 1875' is conserved in the Národni Technické Muzeum, Prague. See Michal, 16–7.

Fire-clocks Catalogue Candle and Lamp-clocks

21 Reconstruction of a Saxon Candle-Clock

20th century
Wood, plastics, and paper
Overall height 13½ in. (343 mm)
Not signed
Inventory D1006

The candle is divided into twelve equal parts by painted rings and enclosed in a case for protection from air currents. The device is a modern realization of the candle-clock of Alfred the Great *c.* 878. There is a similar, but larger, example of this device in the William Barclay Stephens Collection, California Academy of Sciences, San Francisco.

Provenance: Hagans Clock Manor Museum, Evergreen, Colorado.

figure 72. Catalogue no. 21:
Reconstruction of a
Saxon candle-clock.

22 Candle Timekeeper

20th century
Wood, with brass candle holder and
scrolled steel support
Overall length 11½ in. (292 mm)
Not signed, but possibly by Pearson Page Co.,
Birmingham
Inventory D1028

The turned candlestick has a horizontal arm attached at one side on the end of which an hour scale is mounted. Between the candle and the hour scale is a 'T'-shaped shadow-vane. When the candle is lit, the changing position of the shadow on the scale as the candle burns and its height diminishes indicates the time.[24]

Provenance: Hagans Clock Manor Museum, Evergreen, Colorado.

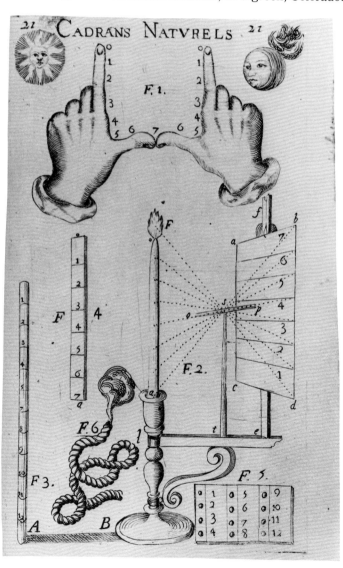

figure 73. A candle shadow clock.
From Bobynet, pl. 21.

24. A similar device is described by Wenham, 85, and dated to the 18th century. For a detailed description of its construction, see Bobynet, 305–8. Although this is the earliest description of the device yet known, it would be rash to consider Bobynet as its inventor. Two devices of this kind are shown in a *c.* 1920 catalogue of Pearson Page Co. The present example combines attributes from each.

figure 74. Catalogue no. 22:
Candle timekeeper.

23 Lamp Timekeeper

Late 18th or 19th century[25]
Pewter and glass
Overall height 12½ in. (318 mm)
Not signed
Inventory SGA 2

The lamp consists of turned single stem with circular base and a small boat-shaped horizontal body piece to carry the wick. Immediately above this is screwed the glass oil reservoir which has two vertical strips on each side, one carrying an hour scale VI-XII-VII for the night hours, the other carrying a small handle.[26]

figure 75. Catalogue no. 23: Lamp timekeeper.

25. On stylistic grounds alone it is virtually impossible to determine the place of origin of pewter lamp timepieces. Although the majority of them are perhaps Dutch and German, there is evidence that they were used in England (Walker and Ashburne's advertisements), Italy (an example signed Antonio Camona, now in the Museo della Scienza, Milan), Japan (example by Hisashige Tanaka, 1837, now in the Musée de l'Horlogerie de la Ville du Locle), and Spain. No attempt, therefore, has been made to ascribe an origin to the pieces here described.
26. For a closely similar example, but with hour scale divided IV–XII–IX and dated *c.* 1750, now in the Uhrensammlung Kellenberger, Winterthur, see Weiss, 29.

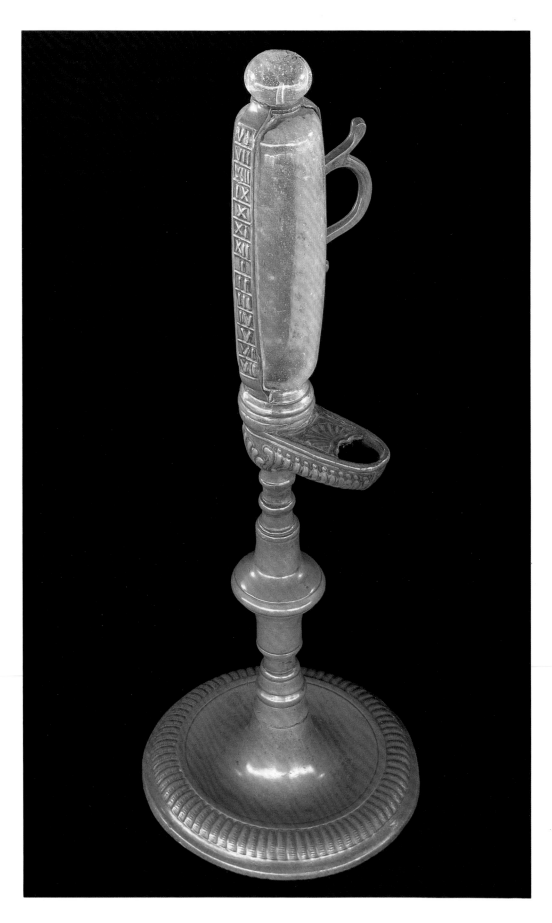

24. Lamp Timekeeper

? 19th century
Glass and pewter
Overall height 19⅛ in. (486 mm)
Not signed
Inventory 94

A short plain cylindrical column mounted on a turned circular base terminates in an oil reservoir from which a tubular arm extends to one side, carrying the wick. Mounted on this arm is a globular glass shade. Mounted above the oil reservoir is a long glass tube engraved with a scale for the twenty-four hours (I-XII/I-XII). Since such timekeepers were primarily intended for use at night, it is unusual to find them with a full 24-hour scale.

figure 76. Catalogue no. 24: Lamp timekeeper.

25. Lamp Timekeeper

? 19th century
Pewter and glass with leather washers and
copper sleeve for the wick
Overall length of body approx. 10 in. (254 mm)
Overall height with bowl 17¼ in. (438 mm)
Not signed
Inventory 1511

The clog-shaped reservoir body tapers to a curved point at one end to carry the wick. Screwed into the top is a ring carrying a glass column graduated in hours V-XII-IX. There is a screw cap at the top to enable the instrument to be filled. Mounted on the body on either side of the column are rings for a suspension chain, and a further ring set underneath carries a ballast tray with spout-shaped corners.

figure 77. Catalogue no. 25:
Lamp timekeeper.

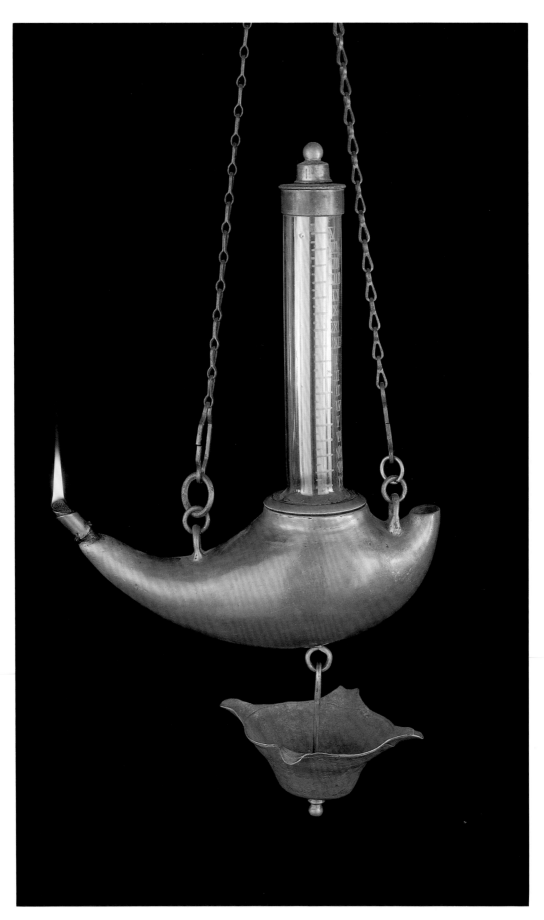

26. Lamp Timekeeper

? 19th century
Pewter and glass
Overall height 13½ in. (343 mm)
Not signed
Inventory D1038

The plain tapering single stem lamp has a circular base and horizontal body piece with hinged lid for the wick. Screwed above this is a bulbous reservoir of ribbed glass with a vertical strip carrying an hour scale (7-12-5) for the night hours. The accuracy of the device is diminished by the shaping of the reservoir.

Provenance: Hagans Clock Manor Museum, Evergreen, Colorado.

figure 78. Catalogue no. 26: Lamp timekeeper.

27. Italian Lamp Timekeeper

? 19th century
Pewter and glass
Overall height 16 in. (406 mm)
Stamped on the edge of the base:
'Fin Pietro Scalione'

Inventory 2394

Consisting of a turned single-stem stand flaring out at the bottom onto an octagonal base, this lamp has a boat-shaped horizontal body piece which carries the wicks, is set immediately below the glass oil reservoir, and has hinged lids. This is surrounded by three vertical strips, the outer two graduated VI-XI-VI, and the center VII-XII-VII. One ungraduated strip carries a handle.

figure 79. Catalogue no. 27: Italian lamp timekeeper.

28. American Oil-lamp Clock

c. 1871
Brass and glass
Height 6¾ in. (170 mm)
Marked: Time & Light Pride of America
Grand-Vals Perfect Time Indicating Lamp
Inventory D1007

The moulded glass base acts as the oil reservoir and support for the brass wick holder. The wick mount is adjustable by a serrated wheel mounted on an arbor that can be revolved. Surmounting the wick is an opaque white lampshade, and moulded in the glass of the reservoir is an hour scale 8-6. The lamp is lit at night, and the falling level of the oil in the reservoir column allows the time to be known.

The Grand-Vals time lamp was patented on 18 April 1871, and additional patents were taken out in 1891 and 1896. A similar example is in the Smithsonian Institution, Washington, D.C.[27]

figure 80. Catalogue no. 28: American oil-lamp clock.

29. French Candle Timekeeper

c. 1875
Cast and gilt brass and glass
Height 16¹/₄ in. (425 mm)
Not signed, marked: Brevete LF S.G.D.F.
Inventory D1005

Normal decoration enhances the cast base, and there is a single column stand shaped as an inverted cone. The candle holder support has lion-head decorations and hanging chains, and the opaque glass globe is enamelled with an hour scale (I-XII) reading to fifteen minutes. Inside the column stand there is a cylindrical brass case. The candle is carried in this inner case on a spring-loaded block of wood, and is held down, under tension, by a cap with a bayonet type of fastener, with adjustable jaws. The opaque globe sits on a mount attached to the inner case. Joining the spring and the block of wood is a piece of metal with a small lug. The lug rides in a spiral groove running once round the circumference of the inner case, along its length. The inside of the stand has two grooves: one, a spiral cut in the opposite direction to the spiral on the inner case, the other a vertical groove running the length of the stand. A pointer is fixed to a ring rigidly attached to the stand. The sequence of action can be seen in fig. 81.

figure 81. As the candle burns, fresh candle is automatically pushed up by the pressure of the spring. At the same time, the lug— which rides in the grooves of both inner case and stand— moves up the grooves, forcing the inner case to rotate. If the lug is riding the outer vertical groove, the opaque globe will rotate 180° in front of the fixed pointer, indicating a 6-hour duration. If the lug rides the spiral groove, the globe will make a complete revolution, indicating a 12-hour duration. The adjustable jaws on the bayonet mount possibly were used to hold different-sized candles; if so, one burned for 6 hours and a larger one burned for 12 hours.

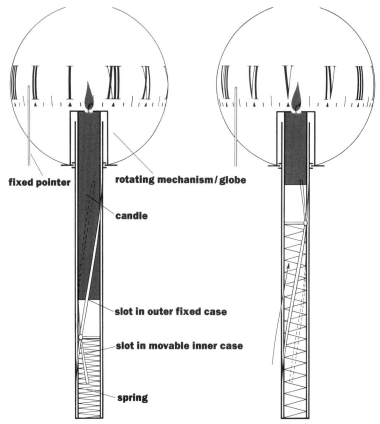

fixed pointer · rotating mechanism/globe · candle · slot in outer fixed case · slot in movable inner case · spring

figure 82 (opposite). Catalogue no. 29: French candle timekeeper.

Incense-clocks

Although methods of using fire for time measurement were common to both the East and the West, use of incense for this purpose seems to have been confined to China, Japan and Korea.[28] It was particularly associated with Buddhism and time measurement in a religious context. The commonest form, and perhaps the earliest, was an adaptation of the graduated candle. A stick of incense was prepared from hard paste and graduated into intervals that would slowly burn. Or the incense paste was cast in a decorative spiral that could be hung on a small stand.[29] The antiquity of the incense stick time-teller is evidently great. It is mentioned in a poem of You Jiangu (*fl. c.* A.D. 520), and may have been used earlier.[30] There are numerous references in medieval Chinese writings, and in accounts by European missionaries and other travellers in the East from the 16th to the 20th centuries.

During the Tang dynasty (A.D. 618–906) an improved form of incense timekeeper was developed, the *xiangyin* (incense seal). This, which Bedini considers to have been 'unquestionably of Buddhist origin,'[31] was developed probably in the 11th century A.D. in two main forms, the Hundred-gradation incense seal (fig. 83), and the Five-watch incense seal. According to Shen Li, a Chinese prefect and hydraulic engineer, the Hundred-gradation seal was invented by an official called Mei Ji (Plumtrees Torrent) as a night timekeeper, in A.D. 1073, a year when there was a long drought and clepsydrae could not be used. The following year a craftsman, Wu Zhengzhong, made an improved example of the seal which he presented to Shen Li together with a recipe for the incense to be used with it. The Hundred-gradation incense seal divided day and night into twelve *shi* (double hours) and into 100 *ke*. Each *shi* therefore equalled 8⅓ *ke*. A trail of incense was laid in a complicated maze-like pattern, which, when ignited[32] slowly burnt, indicating the time (fig. 83). The Five-watch incense seal was developed specifically to measure time at night using the five *geng* divisions. Inevitably the length of each time period would vary with the seasons of the year, and the Five-watch seal therefore required several different seals for the different seasons.[33] Although no early incense seals have survived, a number of relatively recent and less complicated examples are known in various forms. A further variant form, ultimately derived from China, was used in Japan, although exclusively in Buddhist

27. Bedini (III), 37 & fig. 15.
28. There is no known record of incense time measurement in Manchuria, Mongolia, or Tibet. Bedini (II), 38, on which this introduction is largely based and to whom I am indebted for reading and commenting on earlier drafts.
29. Planchon, 255.
30. Bedini (II), 6 & *cf.* 14.
31. *Ibid.*, 7.
32. The device could in fact be started at any time one wished. As Shen Li pointed out, 'We set neither an end point nor a place for starting the fire.' Bedini (II), 10.
33. For a detailed description, *Ibid.*, 12–16.

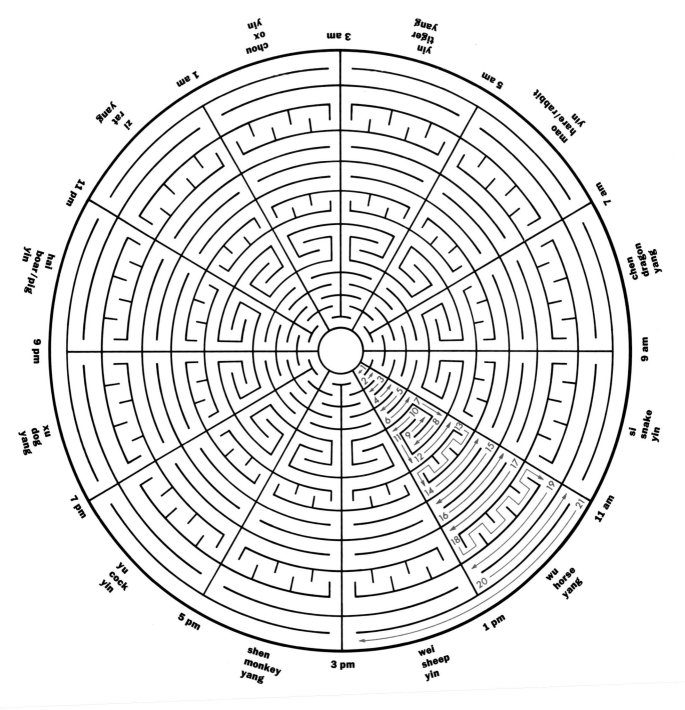

figure 83. Hundred-gradation incense
seal. Diagram after Bedini (II).

temples. Japanese examples differ from the Chinese in being larger,
and are usually made of wood (catalogue no. 33).

Despite the development of the incense seal, the simpler graduated incense stick continued in use. By at least the 18th century
A.D. it had been adapted to provide an aural time signal. The stick
was laid horizontally in a boat-shaped vessel. Across the stick
strings were laid, having small bells tied to each. As the stick burnt
away, the string would also burn, thus causing the bells to fall onto a
metal plate below to indicate the hour (catalogue nos. 31 & 32). In a
further simple form one or several graduated sticks were set upright in a bowl of ash. This form of timekeeper seems also to have
been widely used in Korea from the 7–8th centuries onwards.

Fire-clocks Catalogue
Incense-clocks

30. Chinese Incense Seal Timekeeper

Ming dynasty (A.D. 1388–1644)
Copper and brass
Overall length 11½ in. (292 mm)
Not signed
Inventory 1182

The box is curved in the form of a *Ju'i* sceptre.[34] Into it fits a tray into which fits an inner tray with an elaborately pierced base and with a lifting piece at each end. Above this tray fits a lid with two handles. The box is closed by an outer lid pierced with an archaic inscription.

Another seal of this form, but made of Paktong, with an identical inscription and piercing is now in the collection of E. S. Jones, Los Angeles, California.[35] Several other examples in different metals also exist in public and private collections.

34. According to Bedini (II) 20, this symbol derives from the sacred fungus *lingzhi (Polyporus lucidus)* and is a Daoist emblem of long life.
35. *Ibid.*, 21.

figure 84. Catalogue no. 30:
Chinese incense-seal timekeeper.

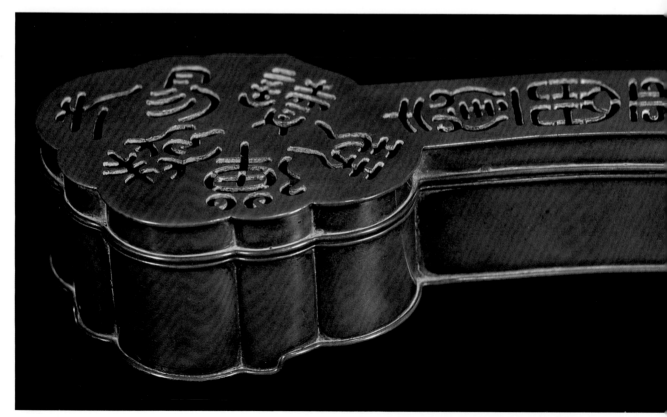

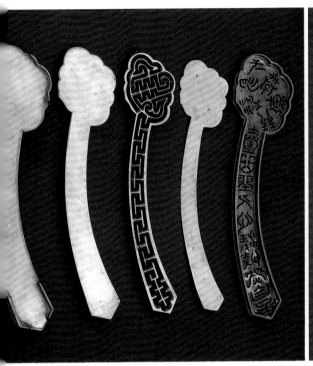

figure 85. Catalogue no. 30.
Dismantled.

31. Chinese Incense Timekeeper

18th or early 19th century
Wood, lacquered black and gold; painted red
and gold, and pewter
Overall length 26½ in. (673 mm)
Not signed
Inventory 1771

A boat-shaped open body is carved in the form of a crouching dragon with open mouth and exaggerated backward sloping ears. The body of the dragon is adorned on each side with a garden scene with figures and small buildings. Pewter inner tray with nine 'U'-shaped cross wires carrying an incense stick.[36]

figures 86 & 87. Catalogue no. 31:
Chinese incense timekeeper.
Top view and side view.

36. For a closely similar dragon shape but without the pictorial scene, see Bedini (II), fig. 25. The decoration is highly unusual and may, according to Bedini (personal communication 29 February 1980), be unique.

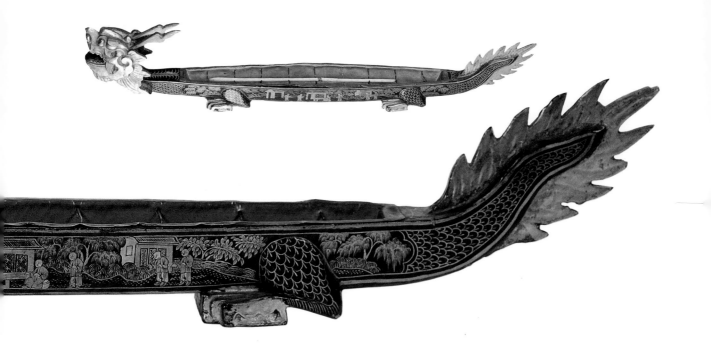

32. Southern Chinese or Japanese Incense Timekeeper

18th or early 19th century
Wood, lacquered black with red and gold;
pewter inner liner
Overall length 20¾ in. (527 mm)
Inscribed inside the body:

Inventory 1088

Scrolled and floral decoration adorn the sides of the boat-shaped open body of this timekeeper. At each end is a semi-seated figure, that at the front is leaning on his left knee and is hatless, that at the back is kneeling on his right knee and has a hat. A rod of some kind was originally held in the free hand of each figure. Pewter inner tray originally with nine 'U'-shaped cross wires (three missing) to carry an incense stick. All the brass bells which give the time signal are now missing. An unusual, perhaps unique, variant of the 'dragon-boat' timekeeper. The character inside the body in Japanese would read *Shigeru* – a popular first name, perhaps that of the owner.

figure 88. Catalogue no. 32:
Southern Chinese or Japanese
incense timekeeper.

33. Japanese Incense Timekeeper (*Koban Dokei*)

? 18th century
Wood lacquered black
Overall height 18¹⁄₈ in. (460 mm); base
13¹⁄₈ × 13¹⁄₈ in. (333 mm × 333 mm)
Ash box 11³⁄₄ in. × 11³⁄₄ in. (299 mm × 299 mm)
Inscribed on each of the storage drawers:
'Kangoro Isuka' (a personal name)
and 'Kamincho Shinjuku' (a district of Tokyo)

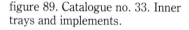
Inventory 957

S et into a square hole cut in the top of the box is a column that carries two decoratively stepped pyramids, the upper of which is inverted and carries the detached ash box. A lid with squared grill nests on the ash box as protection from draughts and accidental disturbance. Accompanying the timepiece are the following accessories:

1. A hand rake for the ash with four prongs, probably a replacement.

2. A tamper and leveller with a smaller blade for clearing the grooves of the template.

3. The incense template.

When the *koban dokei* is used, the ashes are raked smooth and the pattern template pressed over them four times, being fitted once into each corner by means of a groove which fits over the edge of the ash receptacle. An impression is made with the tamper. Incense is then placed in the channel so made, and tablets marked with the animal (zodiacal) signs for the hour are sometimes set upright at intervals along its course. The incense is ignited and the protective grill set in place.

Provenance: Collected in Japan in 1973.[37]

figure 89. Catalogue no. 33. Inner trays and implements.

37. A closely similar example is illustrated by Bedini (II), 37 & fig. 39, who gives a more detailed description.

figure 90. Catalogue no. 33:
Japanese incense timekeeper
(koban dokei).

34. Japanese Incense Timekeeper

Of uncertain date
Paktong and copper
2¹³/₁₆ × 3¾ in. × 2⁹/₁₆ in. (71 mm × 95 mm × 66 mm)
Inscribed on the sides
Inventory 3149

The rectangular box is composed of two trays and a lid. The trays and lid stack one on top of the other. The method of use is similar to that for catalogue nos. 33 and 35. The following accessories are present: incense template, tamper, shovel. The outside is inscribed with archaic characters.

figure 91 (left). Catalogue no. 34. Dismantled. From top: lid, template, tray, bottom tray with implements.
figure 92 (above right). Catalogue no. 34: Japanese incense timekeeper.
figure 93 (right). Catalogue no. 34. Other three sides.

35. Chinese Incense Seal

19th century
Paktong
Height 2¹⁵/₁₆ in. (78 mm)
Diameter 3⁹/₁₆ in. (90 mm)
Not signed or inscribed
Inventory 346-1

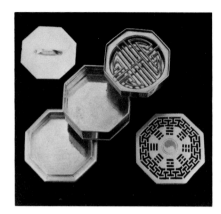

figure 94. Catalogue no. 35.
Inner trays.

The octagonal box has four feet, each pierced with two holes. Above this rests a storage box in which rests the ash tray together with a template. This pattern is a formalization of the Chinese character for 'long life.' There is a perforated lid fitting over the whole, and a tamper. The lid is decorated with the circle of *yang* and *yin* at the centre, surrounded by the eight trigrams. *Yang* and *yin* are the two opposed fundamental principles or forces of traditional Chinese cosmology, *yin* being dark, wintry, cold, weak, damp, even-numbered, and female; *yang* being light, summery, warm, strong, dry, odd-numbered, and male. The trigrams, which derive from the *Yijing* (Book of Changes), are eight symbolic characters which classify and mediate the effects of the movement and counter-movement brought about by the opposition of *yin* and *yang*. The significance of the trigrams can vary with context and they may be identified with the eight wind directions, compass directions, or with divisions of the solar year. The octagon of the eight trigrams surrounding the *yin-yang* circle is often drawn on houses as a charm against evil spirits. In the context of a time-measuring instrument, however, we may assume that they were intended to relate it, and its user, to the cosmological setting.[38]

The manner of use of the incense seal is the same as for the *koban dokei*. A layer of finely sifted wood ash is placed in the ash tray and pressed down with the tamper. The perforated grid is laid on top of this bed and the channels of the maze-like perforation cleared so that incense may be laid in them level with the top of the grill. Small slivers of bamboo are set upright vertically at intervals in the incense to mark the hours and the grid is removed. The incense is ignited and the lid placed over it to protect from draughts.
Provenance: The collection of Silvio A. Bedini, Washington, D.C.

38. For a more detailed discussion of the trigrams, see Feuchtwang, 71–80.

figure 95. Catalogue no. 35:
Chinese incense seal.

36. Chinese Incense Seal

20th century
Pewter and brass
Height 4½ in. (114 mm)
3⅜ in. square (85 mm)
Signed: Yung Lung Wang Tou Teng Oung Chich[39] (and with a paper label which is a dealer's description of the object)

Inventory 346-2

S imilar in arrangement to catalogue no. 35, this four-part box has as the template pattern a formalized form of the word *chou* (longevity). The central pattern of the lid reads *shuangxi* (double happiness).[40] Both the tamper and the shovel are missing.

Provenance: The collection of Silvio A. Bedini, Washington, D.C. He purchased it in Hawaii from descendants of an *emigré* Chinese family who had carried it with them from China. The descendants, not knowing its purpose, used it to burn incense as a defence against insects.

figure 96. Catalogue no. 36. Inner trays and lid.

39. Mary Tregear, Ashmolean Museum, Oxford, provides the following note: 'Yung Lung Wang Tou. This is a very auspicious name, something like "eternal hope and riches," and the Tou is literally a measure, like a corn measure, and so I think this is the name of a shop. Teng Oung Chieh, the last word meaning street, and so this is an address.'
40. For a very similar example now in The Science Museum, London, see Lloyd, 113.

figure 97. Catalogue no. 36:
Chinese incense seal.

Appendix

Hour systems

At an early date in Babylon, a division of the period of the day and night into twelve equal parts (double hours) was used. This system, however, was not widely employed elsewhere in the ancient world, although it may have been transmitted to China. More common were the systems of *equal* and *unequal* hours. *Equal* hours are the divisions of time obtained when the whole period of daylight and darkness is divided into 24 equal parts. Each part is 60 minutes long. *Unequal* hours are the divisions of time obtained when the period of daylight is divided into twelve equal parts and the period of night is divided into twelve equal parts. These hours are not equal to each other except at the equinoxes, when the period of daylight and the period of darkness are exactly equal. Because of the gradual change in the lengths of the day and night with the seasons, the length of the unequal-hours will also gradually change from day to day.

Equal hours were normally used for astronomical purposes until their gradual adoption for civil use in Europe from the 14th century onwards. In antiquity the unequal-hour system was that employed for everyday purposes, although this does not seem to have displaced the older method of indicating time by reference to some repetitive event such as cock-crow, time when the cattle go to water, or lamp-lighting,[1] until the Hellenistic period. Unequal hours were the normal system of time measurement in the Byzantine Empire, medieval Europe, and in Islam until recent times.

In China[2] three main systems of time measurement existed. One system divided the complete period from midnight to midnight into 100 *ke* (notches or gradations). A second system divided the midnight-to-midnight period into twelve *shi* (double hours), the first of which was divided by midnight. Each *shi* was given the name of one of the signs of the Chinese zodiac. The sequence was therefore:

11 pm - 1 am	*zi*	rat		11 am - 1 pm	*wu*	horse
1 am - 3 am	*chou*	ox		1 pm - 3 pm	*wei*	sheep
3 am - 5 am	*yin*	tiger		3 pm - 5 pm	*shen*	monkey
5 am - 7 am	*mao*	hare		5 pm - 7 pm	*you*	cock
7 am - 9 am	*chen*	dragon		7 pm - 9 pm	*xu*	dog
9 am - 11 am	*si*	snake		9 pm - 11 pm	*hai*	boar

1. Such systems survived alongside the numeral systems. For numerous examples, see Nillson, 30–44.
2. For greater detail, see Bedini (II), 40–1.

A third system divided the night, from sunset to sunrise, into five equal parts called *geng*:

rigu	sunset
hun	dusk
chugeng	10 *ke* after dusk
diadan	period of waiting for dawn
xiao	dawn

In India, from at least the 4th or 5th century, the day was usually divided into 60 equal parts called *Ghatīka* or *nāḍi*. According to the *Sūrya Siddhānta*[3]:

$$6 \text{ } prana \text{ (respirations)} = 1 \text{ } vin\bar{a}di$$
$$60 \text{ } vin\bar{a}di = 1 \text{ } n\bar{a}di$$
$$60 \text{ } n\bar{a}di = 1 \text{ day}$$

A similar system is described in the *'Āïn-i-Akbarī*,[4] but using the term *ghāṭi* for *nāḍi* and *pul* for *vināḍi*.

3. Burgess, 149.
4. Gladwin, iii, 10ff.

Glossary

Listed here are the few technical expressions that it was impossible to avoid using in the present work. The basic astronomy underlying early instruments and clocks is explained in appendices to parts 1 and 2 of Volume I of this catalogue. Horological terms will be defined more fully in those volumes of the series concerned with mechanical horology.

Declination	angular distance of a heavenly body north or south of the equator
Detent	something which arrests motion, a locking-piece
Ecliptic	the imaginary path of the sun around the earth
Epicycloid	a curve generated by a point in the circumference of a circle as it rolls upon another circle
Equinoctial Equatorial	terms relating to the celestial equator
Escapement	that device in the gear-train of a clock, watch, or chronometer which regulates the driving force
Jacks	automata which give visual or aural indication of the hour
Meridian	great circle of the heavens passing through the zenith and the poles
Noria	water-lifting wheel
Pinion	a small toothed wheel; the smaller of toothed wheels working together
Polar-mounting	a mounting on the axis of the celestial poles
Solstitial colure	great circle of the heavens passing through the poles and the two points where the tropics of Cancer and Capricorn meet the ecliptic

Bibliography of works cited

ABELER — JÜRGEN ABELER, *5000 Jahre Zeitmessung: Dargestellt im Wuppertaler Uhrenmuseum an der Privatsammlung der Uhrmacher-und Goldschmiedefamilie Abeler,* Wuppertal, 1968.

AKED — J.R.A. AKED, 'Sand-glasses of the Historisches Uhrenmuseum Wuppertal, Germany,' *Antiquarian Horology,* ix, 1979, 293–8.

ALEXANDRE — JACQUES ALEXANDRE, *Traité général des horloges,* Paris, 1734.

D'ALLEMAGNE — HENRI RENE D'ALLEMAGNE, *Les accessoires du costume et du mobilier depuis le treizième jusqu'au milieu du dix-neuvième siècle,* Paris, 1928.

ARMSTRONG & McKCAMP — JOE E. ARMSTRONG & JOHN McKCAMP II, 'Notes on a waterclock in the Athenian Agora,' *Hesperia,* 46, 1977, 147–61.

ARDAILLON — E. ARDAILLON, 'Horologium,' in C. Daremberg & E. Saglio (eds.). *Dictionnaire des antiquités grecques & romaines d'après les textes et les monuments,* 4 vols, Paris, 1877, 260–4.

ATHENAEUS — CHARLES BURTON GULICK (ed. & tr.), *Athenaeus, 'The Deipnosophists,'* 6 vols., London & New York, 1927–41.

BAILLIE — G. H. BAILLIE, *Clocks and Watches: an Historical Bibliography,* London, 1951.

BARGES — J.J.L. BARGES, *Tlemcen, ancienne capitale du royaume de ce nom: sa topographie, son histoire, description de ses principaux monuments, anecdotes, légendes et récits divers* . . . , Paris, 1859.

BASSERMANN-JORDAN — ERNST VON BASSERMANN-JORDAN, *The Book of Old Clocks and Watches* (rev. by H. von Bertele), London & New York, 1964.

BECKMANN — JOHN BECKMANN, *A History of Inventions, Discoveries, and Origins,* 4th edit. (tr. William Johnston, rev. and enl. by William Francis & J.W. Griffith), 2 vols., London, 1846.

BEDINI (I) — SILVIO A. BEDINI, 'The Compartmented Cylindrical Clepsydra,' *Technology & Culture,* 3, Spring 1962, 115–41.

BEDINI (II) — SILVIO A. BEDINI, 'The Scent of Time,' *Transactions of the American Philosophical Society,* n.s. 53, 1963.

BEDINI (III) — SILVIO A. BEDINI, 'Adventures in Time VI: Time and Light,' *La Suisse Horlogère,* 79 & 80, December 1964 & June 1965, 29–38 & 25–30.

BEDINI (IV) — SILVIO A. BEDINI, 'The Seventeenth Century Table Clepsydra,' *Physis. Rivista Internazionale di Storia della Scienza,* x., 1968.

DE BEER (I) — E.S. DE BEER, 'The Notices of Rome in *The Unfortunate Traveller,'* *Notes & Queries,* clxxxv, 1941, 67–70.

DE BEER (II) — E.S. DE BEER (ed.), *The Diary of John Evelyn,* Oxford, 5 vols. 1955.

BENNENDORF, WEISS, & REHM — O. BENNENDORF, E. WEISS, & A. REHM, 'Zur Salzburger Bronzescheite mit Sternbildern,' *Jahreshefte des Österreichischen archäologischen Instituts in Wien,* V, 1902.

BILFINGER   G. BILFINGER, *Die Zeitmesser die Antiken Völker,* Stuttgart, 1886.

BLANCKLEY   THOMAS BLANCKLEY, *A Naval Expositor,* London, 1750.

BOAS   MARIE BOAS, 'Hero's Pneumatica: A Study in its Transmission and Influence,' *Isis,* 40, 1949, 38–48.

BOBYNET   PIERRE BOBYNET, *l'Horographie ingenieuse contenant des connaissances et des curiostez agreable dans la composition des cadrans . . .,* Paris, 1663.

BORCHARDT   LUDWIG BORCHARDT, *Die Altägyptische Zeitmessung (Die Geschichte der Zeitmessung und der Uhren,* ed. by Ernst von Bassermann-Jordan, Bd. I., Lg. B), Berlin & Leipzig, 1920.

BRETT   GERARD BRETT, 'The Automata in the Byzantine "Throne of Solomon," ' *Speculum,* xxix, 1954, 477–87.

BRIEUX & MADDISON   ALAIN BRIEUX & FRANCIS MADDISON, *Répertoire des facteurs d'astrolabes et de leurs œuvres, première partie, Islam, plus Armenie, Géorgie et Inde Hindoue,* Paris (forthcoming).

BRITTEN   F.J. BRITTEN, *Old Clocks and Watches and their Makers,* 3rd edit., London, 1911.

BROCKHAUS   OTTO LEHMANN-BROCKHAUS, *Lateinische Schriftquellen zur Kunst in England, Wales, und Schottland vom Jahr 901 bis zum Jahr 1307,* 5 vols. Munich, 1955–60.

BRUCE   J. DOUGLAS BRUCE, 'Human Automata in Classical Tradition and Medieval Romance,' *Modern Philology,* X, 1912–13, 511–26.

BRUMBAUGH   R.S. BRUMBAUGH, 'Plato and the History of Science,' *Studium Generale: Zeitschrift für die Einheit der Wissenschaften im Zusammenhang ihrer Begriffsbildungen und Forschungs-methoden,* xiv, 1961, 520–7.

BURGESS   EBENEZER BURGESS, 'Translation of the Sûrya-Siddhânta, a textbook of Hindu Astronomy with Notes and an Appendix,' *Journal of the American Oriental Society,* vi, 1860, 141–498.

CALHOUN   GERTRUDE L. CALHOUN, *Hour-Glass Lure and Lore,* New Jersey, 1938.

CAMPBELL   LILY B. CAMPBELL, *Scene and Machine on the English Stage in the Renaissance,* Cambridge (Mass.), 1934.

CAPART   JEAN CAPART, 'Horloges Egyptiennes,' *Bulletin des Musées Royaux d'Art et d'Histoire,* 3rd ser., x, 1938, 49–54.

CASSIDY   THOMAS CASSIDY, 'Letter to the Editor,' *Horological Journal,* October, 1955, 658.

CHAMBERS   R.W. CHAMBERS (ed.), *The Book of Days. A Miscellany of Popular Antiquities in Connection with the Calendar,* 2 vols., London & Edinburgh, 1863–4.

CHAPUIS   ALFRED CHAPUIS, *de Horologiis in Arte,* Lausanne, 1954.

CHAYETTE-SABRIER   *Horlogerie de Collection . . .vente aux encherès . . .Paris Nouveau Drouot . . .3 juin 1982–par le ministère de Me Hervé Chayette assisté de M. Jean-Claude Sabrier,* Paris, 1983.

CHOU   LIU HSIEN CHOU, 'On the Chinese Invention of Time-keeping Apparatus,' *Actes du VIIIe Congrès International d'histoire des Sciences,* 2 vols. Florence & Paris, 1958. I. 329–40.

CLAGETT   MARSHALL CLAGETT, 'The Life and Works of Giovanni Fontana,' *Annali dell' Instituto e Museo di Storia della Scienza di Firenze,* I, 1976, 5-28.

C.N.A.M.   CONSERVATOIRE NATIONALE DES ARTS ET METIERS, *Catalogue du Musée Section JB Horlogerie,* Paris, 1949.

COMBRIDGE (I)   J.H COMBRIDGE, 'The Celestial Balance: a practical Reconstruction,' *Horological Journal,* 104, 1962, 82-6.

COMBRIDGE (II)   J.H. COMBRIDGE, 'Letter to the Editor,' *Antiquarian Horology,* viii, 1974, 775.

COMBRIDGE (III)   J.H. COMBRIDGE, 'The Astronomical Clocktower of Chang Ssu-Hsun and his Successors A.D. 976 to 1126,' *Antiquarian Horology,* ix, 1975, 288–301.

COMBRIDGE (IV)   J.H. COMBRIDGE, 'Clocktower Millenary Reflections,' *Antiquarian Horology,* xi, 1979, 604–8.

COMBRIDGE (V)   J.H. COMBRIDGE, 'Addenda: the 13th Century "King Hezekiah" Water Clock,' *Antiquarian Horology,* xii, 1980, 300.

COMBRIDGE (VI)   J.H. COMBRIDGE, 'Chinese Steelyard Clepsydras,' *Antiquarian Horology,* xii, 1981, 530–5.

COOMARASWAMY   A.K. COOMARASWAMY, *The Treatise of al-Jazarī on Automata,* Boston, 1924.

COX   J. CHARLES COX, *Pulpits, Lecterns, & Organs in English Churches,* Oxford, 1915.

CUMMING   H. SYER CUMMING, 'On Hour-Glasses,' *Journal of the British Archaeological Society,* xxix, 1874, 130–7.

D.   P.D. 'Clepsydres à pendules,' *Science Progres, La Nature,* 97, 1969, 29.

DARESSY   G. DARESSY, 'Deux Clepsydres antiques,' *Bulletin de l'Institut Egyptien,* 5th ser., ix, 1916, 5–16.

DESTOMBES   MARCEL DESTOMBES, *Un Globe céleste inédit de l'Epoque Seljoukide* (537 de l'Hégire),' *Actes du ixe Congrès International d'Histoire des Sciences,* Barcelona-Madrid, 447–52.

DIELS (I)   H. DIELS, 'Über die Prokop beschreibene Kunstuhr von Gaza,' *Abhandlungen d. Preuss. Akad. d. Wiss. Berlin* (Phil. Hist. K), 1917, no. 7.

DIELS (II)   H. DIELS, *Antike Technik,* 2 vols., 1920.

DODGE   BAYARD DODGE, 'The Sạbians of Harrān,' in Fûad Sarrâf & Suha Tamian (eds.) *American University of Beirut Festival Book (Festschrift),* Beirut, 1967, 59–87.

DOWNEY (I)   GLANVILLE DOWNEY, 'Pappus of Alexandria on Architectural Studies,' *Isis,* 38, 1947–8.

DOWNEY (II)   GLANVILLE DOWNEY, 'Byzantine Architects their Training and Methods,' *Byzantion,* xviii, 1948, 99–118.

DRACHMANN (I)   A.G. DRACHMANN, 'Hero and Pseudo-Hero's Adjustable Siphon,' *Journal of Hellenic Studies,* 52, 1932, 116–8.

DRACHMANN (II)   A.G. DRACHMANN, *Ktesibios, Philo, and Heron: A Study in Ancient Pneumatics* (Acta Historica Scientiarum Naturalium et Medicinalium, iv), Copenhagen, 1948.

DRACHMANN (III)   A.G. DRACHMANN, 'The Plane Astrolabe and the Anaphoric Clock, *Centaurus,* iii, 1954, 183–9.

DRACHMANN (IV)   A.G. DRACHMANN, *The Mechanical Technology of Greek and Roman Antiquity,* Copenhagen, 1963.

DROVER (I)   C.B. DROVER, 'A Medieval Monastic Water Clock,' *Antiquarian Horology,* i, 1953–6, 54–8, and partially reprinted in *Antiquarian Horology,* xii, 1980, 165–70.

DROVER (II)   C.B. DROVER, 'The 13th Century "King Hezekiah" Water Clock,' *Antiquarian Horology,* xii, 1980, 160–4.

DROVER ET AL   C.B. DROVER, P.A. SABINE, C. TYLER & P.G. COOLE, 'Sand-Glass "Sand," Historical, Analytical, Practical,' *Antiquarian Horology,* iii, 1960, 62–72.

D.S.B.   CHARLES COULSTON GILLISPIE (editor-in-chief), *Dictionary of Scientific Biography,* 16 vols., New York, 1970–80.

FAIRHOLT   F.W. FAIRHOLT, 'Pulpit Hour-Glasses,' *Journal of the British Archaeological Society,* 3, 1848, 301–10.

FASTES   *Les Fastes du Gothique: Le Siècle de Charles V,* Paris, 1981.

FEUCHTWANG   STEPHAN D.R. FEUCHTWANG, *An Anthropological Analysis of Chinese Geomancy,* Vientiane, 1974.

FLEET   J.F. FLEET, 'The Ancient Indian Water-Clock,' *Journal of the Royal Asiatic Society of Great Britain & Ireland,* 1915, 213–30.

FORBES   E.G. FORBES, 'Mesopotamia and Greek Influences on Ancient Indian Astronomy and on the Work of Aryabhanta,' *Indian Journal of History of Science,* 12, 1978, 150–60.

FORLATTI   PAOLO F. FORLATTI, 'Roman Solar-acoustic Clock in Verona,' *Antiquarian Horology,* ix, 1975, 198–201.

FOTHERINGHAM   J.K. FOTHERINGHAM, 'The Probable Error of a Water-Clock,' *Horological Journal,* 1916, 143–6.

FREEMAN-GRENVILLE   G.S.P. FREEMAN-GRENVILLE, *The Muslim and Christian Calendars,* London, 1963.

GALLON   GALLON, *Machines et inventions approuvées par l'Académie royale des sciences depuis son établissement jusqu'à présent; avec leur descriptions,* 7 vols., Paris, 1735–77.

GERSHENSON & GREENBERG   DANIEL E. GERSHENSON & DANIEL A. GREENBERG, *Anaxogoras and the Birth of Physics,* New York, London, & Toronto, 1964.

GILCHRIST   JOHN GILCHRIST, 'Account of the Hindustanee Horometry, *Asiatick Researches,* v, 1798, 81–9.

GILLE (I)   BERTRAND GILLE, 'Technological Developments in Europe 1100 to 1400,' in Guy S. Metraux & Francois Crouzet, *The Evolution of Science,* New York, 1963.

GILLE (II)   BERTRAND GILLE, *The Renaissance Engineers,* London, 1966.

GILLE (III)   BERTRAND GILLE, *Les Méchaniciens Grecs: la Naissance de la Technologie,* Paris, 1980.

GLADWIN   FRANCIS GLADWIN (tr.), *Ayeen Akbari: or the Institutes of the Emperor Akbar translated from the original Persian,* 3 vols., Calcutta, 1783.

GLICK   THOMAS GLICK, 'Medieval Irrigation Clocks,' *Technology & Culture,* x, 1969, 424–8.

GOEJE M.J. DE GOEJE (ed.), *Bibliotheca geographorum Arabicorum* (8 vols.), 13: al-Muqaddasí, *Descriptio Imperii Moslemici*, Leiden, 1906.

GRENFELL & HUNT B.P. GRENFELL & A.S. HUNT, *The Oxyrynchus Papyri (Part III)*, London, 1903.

GROTZSCH HELMUT GROTZSCH, *Dresden Mathematisch-Physikalischer Salon*, Leipzig, 1978.

GUNTHER R.T. GUNTHER, *Early Science in Oxford: I. Chemistry, Mathematics, Physics, and Surveying* (Oxford Historical Society LXXVII), Oxford, 1923.

D'HAENENS ALBERT D'HAENENS, 'Le Clepsydre de Villers (1267). Comment on mesurait et vivait le temps dans une abbaye cistercienne au XIIIe siècle,' in *Klösterliche Sachkultur des Spätmittelalters: Internationaler Kongress Krems an der Donau 18. bis 21. September, 1978,* Vienna, 1980, 321–42.

HALMA N. HALMA (ed. & tr.), *Les Phénomènes d'Aratus de Soles et de Germanicus César; avec les scholies de Théon, les Catastérismes d'Erathostènes, et la Sphère de Léontius . . .,* Paris, 1821.

HARFORD W.C. HARFORD, 'The Hour Glass,' *The Connoisseur,* March, 1933.

HARRIS L.C. HARRIS, *The Two Netherlanders: Humphrey Bradley and Cornelis Drebbel,* Cambridge, 1961.

HARRISON KENNETH HARRISON, 'Vitruvius and Acoustic Jars in England during the Middle Ages,' *Transactions of the Ancient Monument Society,* N.S. xv, 1968, 48–58.

HARVEY L.P. HARVEY, 'The Alphonsine School of Translators: Translations from Arabic into Castilian produced under the Patronage of Alfonso the Wise of Castile (1221–1251–1284),' *Journal of the Royal Asiatic Society,* N.S. 1977, 109–17.

HASKINS CHARLES HOMER HASKINS, *Studies in the History of Medieval Science,* 2nd edit., Cambridge (Mass.), 1927.

HAVARD HENRI HAVARD, *Les arts de l'ameublement: l'Horlogerie,* Paris, 1928.

HEERS JACQUES HEERS, *Christophe Colombe,* Paris, 1981.

HILL (I) DONALD R. HILL, *The Book of Knowledge of Ingenious Mechanical Devices . . . by Ibn al-Razzāz al-Jazari,* Dordrecht and Boston, 1974.

HILL (II) DONALD R. HILL (ed. & tr.), *On the Construction of Water Clocks: Kitāb Archīmidas fī 'Amal al-Binkamāt,* London, 1976.

HILL (III) DONALD R. HILL, 'A Treatise on Machines by Ibn Mu'ādh Abû 'Abd Allah al-Jayānī,' *Journal for the History of Arabic Science,* I, 1977, 33–44.

HILL (IV) DONALD R. HILL, 'Notice of an important al-Jazari Manuscript,' *Journal for the History of Arabic Science,* II, 1978, 291–8.

HILL (V) DONALD R. HILL, *The Book of Ingenious Devices (Kitab al-Ḥiyal) by the Banū (sons of) Mūsà bin Shàkir,* Dordrecht, 1979.

HILL (VI) DONALD R. HILL, *Arabic Water Clocks,* Aleppo, 1982.

HILL & PAGET-TOMLINSON H.O. HILL & E.W. PAGET-TOMLINSON, *Instruments of Navigation: a Catalogue of Instruments in the National Maritime Museum with Notes on their Use,* London, 1958.

HIND   ARTHUR M. HIND, *Wenceslaus Hollar and his Views of London and Windsor in the Seventeenth Century,* London, 1922.

HINKS   E.L. HINKS, 'Iasos,' *Journal of Hellenic Studies,* viii, 1887, 83–118.

HODGKIN   THOMAS HODGKIN, *The Letters of Cassiodorus, being a condensed translation of the Variae Epistolae of Magnus Aurelius Cassiodorus, Senator,* London, 1886.

HUGHES (I)   G. BERNARD HUGHES, 'Old English Sand-glasses,' *Country Life,* 16 November 1951, 1622–3.

HUGHES (II)   G. BERNARD HUGHES, 'Stands for Georgian Egg-cups,' *Country Life,* 21 November 1968, 1334–5.

HULME (I)   E. WYNDHAM HULME, 'Currency Bars and Water-Clocks. The Verdicts of Archaeology Reviewed,' *Antiquity,* 7, 1933, 61–73.

HULME (II)   E. WYNDHAM HULME, [Rejoinder to the Rejoinder of R.A. Smith], *Antiquity,* 7, 1933, 213–5.

HUSSEY   J.M. HUSSEY (ed.), *The Cambridge Medieval History: IV The Byzantine Empire. Part II. Government, Church, and Civilisation,* Cambridge, 1967, 264–305.

HUXLEY   G.L. HUXLEY, *Anthemius of Tralles,* London, 1959.

JAWAD   NAJI JAWAD, *The Story of Time,* n.p. [?Baghdad], n.d. [?*c.* 1960].

JUNGER   ERNST JUNGER, *Das Sanduhr Buch,* Frankfurt am Main, 1957. French translation: *le Traité du Sablier,* Henri Plard, Paris, 1981.

KELLER(I)   A.G. KELLER, 'Pneumatics, Automata and the Vacuum in the Work of Giambattista Aleotti', *British Journal of the History of Science,* iii, 1967, 338–47.

KELLER (II)   A.G. KELLER, 'Mathematical Technologies and the Growth of the Idea of Technical Progress in the Sixteenth Century', in Allen G. Debus (ed.), *Science, Medicine and Society in the Renaissance; Essays to Honour Walter Pagel,* 2 vols., London, 1972, 11–28.

KENNEDY   E.S. KENNEDY (tr.), *The Exhaustive Treatise on Shadows by Abū al-Rayḥān Muḥammad b. Aḥmad al-Bīrūnī,* 2 vols., Aleppo, 1976.

KHANIKOFF   N. KHANIKOFF, 'Analysis of the Book of the Balance of Wisdom', *Journal of the American Oriental Society,* vi, 1858, 1ff.

KHAWAM   R.R. KHAWAM, 'Les Statues Animées dans les Mille et Une Nuits,' *Annales E.S.C.,* 30, 1975, 1084–104.

AL-KHWARIZMI   ABU 'ABDALLAH AL-KHOWAREZMI, *Liber Mafatih Al-Olum,* G. van Vloten (ed.), Lyden, 1895.

KNOPPE   KARL-ADOLF KNOPPE, *Dürer: the Complete Engravings, Etchings and Woodcuts,* London, 1965.

KURZ   OTTO KURZ, *European Clocks and Watches in the Near East,* London & Leiden, 1975.

LABARTE   JULES LABARTE, *Inventaire du mobilier de Charles V, roi de France,* Paris, 1879.

LANDAU   ROM LANDAU, *Morocco,* London, 1967.

LANG   MABEL LANG, *Waterworks in the Athenian Agora* (American School of Classical Studies at Athens: Excavations in the Athenian Agora, Picture Books II), Princeton, 1968.

LAST   HUGH LAST, 'Empedockles and his Klepsydra Again,' *Classical Quarterly,* xviii, 1924, 169–73.

LATTIN	HARRIET PRATT LATTIN, *The Letters of Gerbert with his Papal Privilege as Sylvester II,* New York, 1959.
LE LOCLE	*Musée d'Horlogerie de la Ville du Locle au Château des Monts,* catalogue, le Locle, n.d.
LEMERLE	P. LEMERLE, *Le premier humanisme byzantin: Notes et remarques sur l'enseignement et la culture à Byzance des origines au Xe siècle,* Paris, 1971.
LLOYD (I)	H. ALAN LLOYD, *Some Outstanding Clocks Over Seven Hundred Years, 1250–1950,* London, 1958.
LLOYD (II)	H. ALAN LLOYD, *The Collector's Dictionary of Clocks and Watches,* Feltham, 1964, 1969.
LOPEZ	R.A. LOPEZ, 'L'Extrême Frontière du Commerce de l'Europe Médiévale,' *Moyen Age,* 69, 1963.
LORCH	R.P. LORCH, 'Al-Khzini's Balance-clock and the Chinese Steelyard Clepsydra,' *Archives Internationales d'Histoire des Sciences,* 31, 1981, 183–9.
LUBKE	ANTON LUBKE, *Die Uhr von der Sonnenuhr zur Atomuhr,* Dusseldorf, 1958.
LUNARDI	HEINRICH LUNARDI, *900 Jahre Nürnberg: 600 Jahre Nürnberger Uhren,* Vienna & Stuttgart, 1974.
McFARLANE	I.D. McFARLANE (ed.), *The 'Délie' of Maurice Scève,* Cambridge, 1966.
McKERROW	R.B. McKERROW (ed.), *The Works of Thomas Nashe* (revised by F.P. Wilson), 5 vols., Oxford, 1958.
MACKENSEN	LUDOLF VON MACKENSEN, 'Neue Ergebnisse zur ägyptischen Zeitmessung. Die Inbetriebnahme und Berechnung der Ältesten erhaltenen Wasseruhr,' *Alte Uhren, Zeitmeßgeräte, wissenschaftliche Instrumente und Automaten,* I, 1978, 13–18.
MADDISON	FRANCIS MADDISON, 'Hugo Helt and the Rojas Astrolabe Projection,' *Agrupamento de Estudos de Cartografia Antiga,* XII, Secçao de Coimbra, 1966.
MADDISON, SCOTT, & KENT	FRANCIS MADDISON, BRYAN SCOTT, & ALAN KENT, 'An Early Medieval Water Clock,' *Antiquarian Horology,* III, 1962, 348–53.
MADDISON & TURNER	FRANCIS MADDISON & ANTHONY TURNER, *Science and Technology in Islam: Catalogue of an Exhibition in the Science Museum, 6 April–31 August 1976* (unpublished).
MARQUARDT	JOACHIM MARQUARDT, *La Vie Privée des Romains* (Victor Henry, tr.), 2 vols., Paris, 1892.
MARTINELLI	DOMENICO MARTINELLI, *Horologi Elementari divisi in quattro parti...,* Venice, 1669.
MAYER (I)	L.A. MAYER, *Islamic Astrolabists and Their Works,* Geneva, 1956.
MAYER (II)	L.A. MAYER, 'Islamic Astrolabists: Some New Materials,' in Richard Ettinghausen (ed.), *Aus der Welt der Islamischen Kunst. Festschrift für Ernst Kühnel zum 75. Geburst am 26.10.1957,* Berlin, 1959.
MICHAL	STANISLAV MICHAL, *Clocks and Watches: a Catalogue of Clocks and Watches, 16th to 20th Century, in the Collections of the National Technical Museum, Prague,* Prague, 1974.

MICHEL   HENRI MICHEL, 'Une clepsydre grecque antique,' *Physis: Rivista Internazionale di Storia della Scienza*, xii, 1970, 363–70.

MILLER   W. MILLER, *The Latins in the Levant. A History of Frankish Greece (1204–1566)*, London, 1908.

MORAUX   P. MORAUX, 'Le reveille-matin d'Aristote,' *Les Etudes Classiques*, xix, octobre 1951.

MILLAS   J.M. MILLAS-VALLICROSA, *Estudios sobre Azarquiel* (Instituto Miguel Asin), Madrid-Granada, 1950.

MILLIKEN   W.M. M[ILLIKEN], 'A Table Fountain of the Fourteenth Century,' *The Bulletin of the Cleveland Museum of Art*, XII, 1925, 36–9.

MRAZ   GOTTFRIED MRAZ, 'The Role of Clocks in the Imperial Honoraria for the Turks,' in Klaus Maurice & Otto Mayr (eds.), *The Clockwork Universe: German Clocks and Automata 1550–1650*, New York, 1980, 37–48.

NAISH   G.P.D. NAISH, 'The "Dyoll" and the bearing Dial,' *Journal of the Institute of Navigation*, vii, 1954, 205–8.

NASR   SEYYED HOSSEIN NASR, *Islamic Science: an Illustrated Study*, London, 1976.

NEEDHAM & WANG LING (I)   JOSEPH NEEDHAM & WANG LING, *Science and Civilization in China, 3, Mathematics and the Sciences of the Heavens and the Earth*, Cambridge, 1959.

NEEDHAM & WANG LING (II)   JOSEPH NEEDHAM & WANG LING, *Science and Civilization in China, 4, Physics and Physical Technology, Part II, Mechanical Engineering*, Cambridge, 1965.

NEEDHAM, WANG LING, & PRICE   JOSEPH NEEDHAM, WANG LING, & DEREK J. DE SOLLA PRICE, *Heavenly Clockwork, the Great Astronomical Clocks of Medieval China*, Cambridge, 1960.

NEUGEBAUER (I)   OTTO NEUGEBAUER, 'Studies in Ancient Astronomy viii: the Water-Clock in Babylonian Astronomy,' *Isis*, xxxvii, 1947, 37–43.

NEUGEBAUER (II)   OTTO NEUGEBAUER, *A History of Ancient Mathematical Astronomy*, 3 vols, New York, Heidelberg, & Berlin, 1975.

NICOLAS   SIR NICHOLAS HARRIS NICOLAS, *A History of the Royal Navy*, 2 vols., London, 1847.

NILSSON   MARTIN P. NILSSON, *Primitive Time-Reckoning. A Study of the Origins and First Development of the Art of Counting Time Among the Primitive and Early Culture Peoples*, Lund, 1920.

NISBET   J. NISBET, *Burma Under British Rule and Before*, 2 vols., London, 1901.

NOBLE & PRICE   JOSEPH V. NOBLE & DEREK J. DE SOLLA PRICE, 'The Water Clock in the Tower of the Winds,' *American Journal of Archaeology*, 72, 1968, 345–55.

NORTH (I)   J.D. NORTH, 'Opus quorundam rotarum mirabilium,' *Physis. Rivista Internazionale di Storia della Scienza*, viii, 1966, 337–72.

NORTH (II)   J.D. NORTH, 'Monasticism and the First Mechanical Clocks,' in J.T. Frazer & N. Lawrence (eds.), *The Study of Time, II* (Proceedings of the Second Conference of the International Society for the Study of Time), New York, Heidelberg, & Berlin, 1975, 381–98.

O'BRIEN — D. O'BRIEN, 'The Effect of a Simile: Empedocles' Theories of Seeing and Breathing,' *Journal of Hellenic Studies,* xc, 1970, 140–79.

OVINGTON — OVINGTON, *Voyage to Surat,* London, 1698.

PARTINGTON — CHARLES F. PARTINGTON, *The British Cyclopedia of the Arts and Sciences,* 2 vols., London, 1835.

PARTRIDGE — ALBERT L. PARTRIDGE, 'Water Clocks,' *Bulletin of National Association of Watch & Clock Collectors of America,* 4, 1950, 138–47.

PERRAULT — CLAUDE PERRAULT, *Lex Dix Livres de Vitruve corrigez et traduite nouvellement en Francais, avec des Notes et des Figures, par M. Perrault,* Paris, 2nd edit. (rev. and enl.), 1684.

PINGREE — DAVID PINGREE, 'The Mesopotamian Origins of early Indian Mathematical Astronomy,' *Journal of the History of Astronomy,* iv, 1973, 1–12.

PINKERTON — J. PINKERTON, *A General Collection of the best and most Interesting Voyages and Travels in all Parts of the World; many of which are now first translated into English,* 9 vols., London, 1811.

PLANCHON — MATTHIEU PLANCHON, *l'Horloge, son histoire rétrospective, pittoresque et artistique,* Paris, n.d. [?1898/99].

PLANTE — JULES PLANTE, *Gnomons et Clepsydres,* Laval, 1890.

PLOT — ROBERT PLOT, *The Natural History of Oxfordshire,* 2nd edit., Oxford, 1705.

POGO — A. POGO, 'Egyptian Water Clocks,' *Isis,* xxv, 1936.

POLTER — RICHARD POLTER, *The Pathway to perfect Sayling. Being a Deliverie in as breefe a Manner as may bee, of the six Principal Pointes or Grounds, concerning Navigation,* London, 1605.

POWER — EILEEN POWER (tr.), *The Goodman of Paris,* London, 1928.

PRICE (I) — DEREK J. DE SOLLA PRICE, 'Mechanical Water Clocks of the 14th Century in Fez, Morocco,' *Actes du Congrès International d'Histoire des Sciences, Ithaca, 26 August–2 September 1959,* Paris, 1962, 599–602.

PRICE (II) — DEREK J. DE SOLLA PRICE, 'On the Origin of Clockwork, Perpetual Motion Devices and the Compass,' *United States National Museum Bulletin 218: Contributions from the Museum of Science and Technology,* Washington, D.C., 1959, 81–112.

PRICE (III) — DEREK J. DE SOLLA PRICE, *Gears from the Greeks: the Antikythera Machine—a Calendar Computer from ca. 80 BC,* New York, 1975.

PROCTOR — EVELYN S. PROCTOR, 'Scientific Works at the Court of Alphonso X of Castile: the King and his Collaborators,' *Modern Language Review,* xl, 1945.

RAMSEY — L.G.G. RAMSEY, 'Holbein's Hourglass?,' *The Connoisseur,* October 1954, 117.

RICO — M. RICO Y SINOBAS (ed.), *Libros del Saber de Astronomía,* 5 vols., Madrid, 1863–67.

ROBERTS — PETER ROBERTS, *The Chronicle of the Kings of Britain to which are added original Dissertations . . . ,* London, 1811.

ROBINSON HENRY S. ROBINSON, 'The Tower of the Winds and the Roman Market Place,' *American Journal of Archaeology*, 47, 1937, 291–335.

DE ROCHAS A. DE ROCHAS, *La Science des Philosophes et l'art des Thaumaturges dans l'Antiquité*, Paris, 1882.

ROCKHILL W.W. ROCKHILL (ed.), *The Journey of William of Rubruck to the Eastern Parts of the World 1253–5*, (Hakluyt Society, 2nd ser., iv) 1900.

ROGERS J.E. THOROLD ROGERS, *A History of Agriculture and Prices in England . . .*, 7 vols., Oxford, 1866 ff.

ROSS W.D. ROSS (ed.), *The Works of Aristotle translated into English*, 10, Oxford, 1921 (1961).

RUELENS CH. RUELENS (ed.), *Le Passetemps de Jehan l'Hermite publié d'après le manuscrit original* (Maatschappij der Antwerpsche Bibliophilen, Uitgaave 17), 2 vols., Antwerp, 1890 & 1896.

SABRA A.I. SABRA, 'A Note on Codex Biblioteca Medicea-Laurenziana Or. 152,' *Journal for the History of Arabic Science*, i, 1977, 276–83.

SALMON SALMON, *L'Art du potier d'etain*, 2 parts., Paris, 1788.

SARTON GEORGE SARTON, *Introduction to the History of Science*, 4 vols., Baltimore, 1937–54.

SAUPPE HERMAN SAUPPE, 'Ein Stelle des Claudius Galenus über die prüfung der Sonnenuhren und die Herstellung einer Wasseruhr,' *Philologus*, xxiii, 1876, 448–54.

SCHMIDT M.C.P. SCHMIDT, *Kulturhistorische Beiträge zur Kenntnis des Griechischen und Römischen Altertums, II. Die Entstehung der Antiken Wasseruhr*, Leipzig, 1912.

SCOTT J.R. SCOTT, *Memorials of the Family of Scott*, London, 1876.

SEARLE MARK SEARLE, *Turnpikes and Toll Bars*, 2 vols., London, 1930.

SHERIDAN PAUL SHERIDAN, 'Les Inscriptions sur Ardoise de l'Abbaye de Villers,' *Annales de la Société d'Archéologie de Bruxelles*, X, 1896, 203–15, 404–51.

SHERWOOD MERRIAM SHERWOOD, 'Magic and Mechanics in Medieval Fiction,' *Studies in Philology*, xliv, 1947, 567–92.

SIDDIQI A. SIDDIQI, 'Construction of Clocks and Islamic Civilization,' *Islamic Culture*, I, 1927, 245–51.

SLEESWYCK ANDRE SLEESWYCK, 'The 13th Century "King Hezekiah" Water-Clock,' *Antiquarian Horology*, xi, 1979, 488–94.

SLOLEY R.W. SLOLEY, 'Ancient Clepsydrae,' *Ancient Egypt*, June, 1924.

SLOLEY & PETRIE R.W. SLOLEY & FLINDERS PETRIE, 'Note on Parabolic Curves,' *Ancient Egypt*, 1927, 16–17.

SMITH (I) R.A. SMITH, 'Timekeepers of the Ancient Britons,' *Proceedings of the Society of Antiquaries*, 2nd ser., xxi, 1907.

SMITH (II) R.A. SMITH, 'Remarks on Vessels found at Wotton, Surrey,' *Proceedings of the Society of Antiquaries*, 2nd ser., 27, 1915.

SMITH (III) R.A. SMITH, *British Museum, Guide to the Early Iron Age*, 2nd edit., 1925.

SMITH (IV) R.A. SMITH, [Rejoinder to E. Wyndham Hulme], *Antiquity*, vii, 1933, 210–13.

SOLENTE	S. SOLENTE (ed.), *Le Livre des Fais et bonnes Meurs du Sage Roy Charles V, par Christine de Pisan* (Société de l'Histoire de France, 256) 2 vols., Paris, 1936.
SOTHEBY	SOTHEBY PARKE BERNET & CO., *The Honeyman Collection of Scientific Books and Manuscripts, Part III. Manuscripts and Autograph Letters of the 12th to the 20th Century,* London, 1979.
SOUBIRAN	JEAN SOUBIRAN (ed.), *Vitruve: de Architecture Livre IX. Texte établi, traduit et commenté,* Paris, 1969.
SPARGO	JOHN WEBSTER SPARGO, *Virgil the Necromancer. Studies in Virgilian Legend* (Harvard Studies in Comparative Literature X), Cambridge (Mass.), 1934.
STCHOUKINE	IVAN STCHOUKINE, 'Un Manuscrit du Traité d'al-Jazarī sur les Automates du VIIᵉ Siècle de l'Hégire,' *Gazette des Beaux Arts,* période vi, xi, 1934, 134–40.
STERNFELD	JOSEPH STERNELD, *Hour Glasses* (Supplement to *Bulletin of National Association of Watch and Clock Collectors*), 1953.
STIMSON	A. STIMSON, 'Logs,' in *An Inventory of the Navigation and Astronomy Collections in the National Maritime Museum, Greenwich,* Greenwich, n.d. [*c.* 1972].
LE STRANGE	G. LE STRANGE, *Baghdad during the Abbasid Caliphate*, Oxford, 1900.
STUART & REVETT	JAMES STUART & NICHOLAS REVETT, *The Antiquities of Athens,* 2nd edit., London, 1762.
TAQIZADEH	S.H. TAQIZADEH, 'Various Calendars and Eras used in the Countries of Islam,' *Bulletin of School of Oriental Studies,* ix, 1938, 903–22 & x, 107–32.
TARDY (I)	TARDY [HENRI LENGELLE], *La Pendule Française,* 3 vols., rev. edit., Paris, 1979.
TARDY (II)	TARDY [HENRI LENGELLE], *Origine de la Mesure du Temps. Du Gnomon à la Montre,* Paris, n.d. [? *c.* 1950].
[TASSIN]	*Histoire Littéraire de la Congrégation de Saint-Maur ordre de St. Benoît,* Brussels, 1770.
THORNDIKE	LYNN THORNDIKE, *A History of Magic and Experimental Science,* 8 vols., New York, 1923–58.
THUREAU-DANGIN	F. THUREAU-DANGIN, 'Notes Assyriologiques LXIX, La Clepsydre chez le Babyloniens,' *Revue d'Assyriologie et d'Archéologie Orientale,* 29, 1932, 133–6.
THURSTON	EDGAR THURSTON, *Ethnographic Notes in Southern India,* Madras, 1906.
TURNER (I)	A.J. TURNER, *Science and Music in Eighteenth Century Bath,* Bath, 1977.
TURNER (II)	A.J. TURNER, ' "The Accomplishment of Many Years": Three Notes towards a History of the Sand-glass,' *Annals of Science,* 39, 1982, 161–72.
TURNER (III)	A.J. TURNER, *Time-Measuring Instruments: Astrolabes and Related Devices* (The Time Museum, Rockford, Illinois: Catalogue of the Collection, Volume I, part 1), Rockford, 1984.

TURPIN   TURPIN, *Histoire civile et naturelle de Siam et des révolutions qui ont boulversée cet empire jusqu'en 1770,* Paris, 2 vols., 1771.

UNGERER   ALFRED UNGERER, *Les Horloges astronomiques et monumentales les plus remarquables de l'Antiquité jusqu'à nos jours,* Strasbourg, 1931.

UTO   *UTO Auktionen: Sale of November 13 1979,* Zurich, 1979.

DE VAUX   BARON CARRA DE VAUX, 'Notice sur deux Manuscrits Arabes,' *Journal Asiatique,* 8ᵉ sér., xvii, 1891, 287–322.

VIARD   JULES VIARD (ed.), *Les Grandes Chroniques de France, III (Charlemagne)* (Société de l'Histoire de France, Paris, 1923).

VILLUENDAS   MARIA VICTORIA VILLUENDAS, 'A Further Note on a Mechanical Treatise contained in Codex Medicea-Laurenziana Or. 152,' *Journal of the History of Arabic Science,* II, 1978, 395–6.

VINCENT   CLARE VINCENT, 'Renaissance Timepieces,' in *The Triumph of Humanism: A Visual Survey of Decorative Arts of the Renaissance* (catalogue of an exhibition organized by the Fine Arts Museum, San Francisco, in the California Palace of the Legion of Honor, 22 October 1977–8 January 1978), San Francisco, 1977.

VIVIELLE   LE COMMANDANT VIVIELLE, 'Les Sabliers horloges de Mer,' *Bulletin Officiel du Yacht Club de France,* 1934.

WALLACE   A.R. WALLACE, *The Malay Archipelago, the Land of the Orang-Utan, and the Bird of Paradise. A Narrative of Travel with Studies of Man and Nature,* 2 vols., London, 1869.

WARD   F.A.B. WARD, *Ministry of Education Science Museum: Handbook of the Collections illustrating Time Measurement; Part I, Historical Review; Part II, Descriptive Catalogue,* London, 1950.

WATERS (I)   D.W. WATERS, 'Early Time and Distance Measurement at Sea,' *Journal of the Institute of Navigation,* viii, 1955.

WATERS (II)   D.W. WATERS, *The Art of Navigation in England in Elizabethan and Early Stuart Times,* London, 1958.

WEISS   ROLF WEISS, *Schweizerische Kunstführer. Herausgegeben von der Gesellschaft für Schweizerische Kunstgeschichte,* Winterthur, 1974.

WENHAM   EDWARD WENHAM, *Old Clocks for Modern Use,* London, 1951.

WERLY   L. MAXE-WERLY, 'Notes sur les objets antiques découverts à Gondrecourt (Meuse) et à Grand (Vosges),' *Memoires de la Société Nationale des Antiquaires de France,* 5, 48, 1887, 170–8.

WHITE (I)   LYNN WHITE JR., *Medieval Technology and Social Change,* Oxford, 1962.

WHITE (II)   LYNN WHITE JR., *Medieval Religion and Technology: Collected Essays,* Berkeley, Los Angeles, & London, 1978.

WIEDEMANN & HAUSER   E. WIEDEMANN & F. HAUSER, 'Uhr des Archimedes und zwei andere Vorrichtungen,' *Nova Acta, Abhandlungen der Kaiser Leopold Carolinus – Deutschen Akademie der Naturforscher,* 103, 1918, n. 2, 164–202.

WOOD   EDWARD J. WOOD, *Curiosities of Clocks and Watches*, London, 1866.

WRIGHT   R.R. WRIGHT (tr.), *The Book of Instruction in the Elements of the Art of Astrology by Abū l-Rayhān Muhammad Ibn Ahmad al-Bīrūnī*, London, 1934.

YATES   FRANCES A. YATES, *Theatre of the World,* London, 1969.

YOUNG   SUZANNE YOUNG, 'An Athenian Clepsydra,' *Hesperia: Journal of the American School of Classical Studies at Athens*, viii, 1939, 274–84.

Concordance

Inventory numbers		Catalogue numbers
31	18	
32	1	
33	2	
78	21	
79	12	
94	24	
115	16	
116	11	
181	5	
343	8	
346–1	35	
346–2	36	
349	7	
369	4	
439	19	
481	17	
494	9	
957	33	
1088	32	
1176	13	
1182	30	
1511	25	
1531	15	
1546	10	
1643	14	
1771	31	
2394	27	
2669	6	
3149	34	
D1004	3	
D1005	29	
D1006	21	
D1007	28	
D1028	22	
D1038	26	
SGA–1	20	
SGA–2	23	

Index

Numbers in *italics* are those of illustrations or their captions. In the alphabetization of Arabic names, which have been indexed under the *Ism ('Alam)* except where some other element is used, e.g. the *nisba* al-Bīrūnī, the particles *al-*, *ar-*, etc., have been ignored, as have the apostrophe, de, du, le, la, l', etc., in European names.

Guo Shoujing 14

Han Gonglian 63, 65
Hansdorfer, George Philip 33
Harmachis 46
Ḥarrān (Carrhae), astrolabe making at 18
Harūn ar-Rashīd 19
Hebrew: MS illustration of sandglass *44*, 76;
    Zohar 21
Hellenistic technology *see under* Greece
Helt, Hugo 120, 121
Hermann of Reichenau 28
Hermite, Jehan l' 120
Hero of Alexandria 6–7, 6 n.35, 15, 17 n.101,
    31–3, 35;
    Construction of Vaults 16;
    Mechanics 19;
    Pneumatica 8, 17;
    translations of 19, 32–3;
    see also pseudo-Hero
Hezekiah, king of Judah, clock of 37 n.182
Hildemar 27
Hire, Philipe de la 82
Hollar, Wenceslaus 81
Hopper, Joachim 120
Horapollo, cited 46 n.208
Hormuz 9
hourglasses: term rejected 75 n.1;
    see sand-glasses
hour scales: for candle shadow clocks *73*, 126;
    for clepsydrae *2*, 5–6, 46 and n.210, 50, 56, 66
hour systems 160–1;
    Babylonian 160;
    Chinese 59, 160–1;
    equal 160;
    Indian 161;
    unequal 2, 5, 46, 56, 160;
    –, rules for adjusting clepsydrae to 26 n.136, 46 n.210
Huygens, Christiaan 72
Hui Yuan 10–11

Iasos, inscription from 3
Ibn al-Furāt 23
Ibn al-Haytham 19 and n.113
Ibn Jubayr 21
Ibn an-Nadīm: *Fihrist* 18
Ibn az-Zarqellu 19

incense-clocks 117, 142–59;
    lingzhi decoration on 146 n.35;
    yin/yang decoration on *94–5*, 156;
    dragon-boat *86–8*, 143, 148–51;
    graduated incense stick 142, 143;
    xiangyin (incense seal) *84*, 142, 146, 156–9;
    –, Fire-watch 142;
    –, Hundred-gradation *83*, 142
India: clepsydrae in 3 and n.12, 4, 10, 11;
    hour system in 161;
    influence on Islam 17
irrigation, clepsydrae used for timing 4 n.25, 10 n.62
Isḥāq b. Sīd 30, 37, 38, 120
Isidore of Miletus 16
Islam: clepsydrae in 4 n.25, 10, 19–25;
    cultural unity of 17;
    Hijra dating used in 17 n.103;
    horological literature of *see under* literature;
    science and technology in 15, 18–21, 24–5;
    West derives horological knowledge from 25, 28, 30;
    Western clockmakers in 25 n.131

Jackson, W.H. & S. 122
Jāḥiẓ: *Kitāb al-Ḥayawān* 18
Japan: incense-clocks in *88*, 142, 142–3, 150–1;
    koban dokei 89–93, 152–6
al-Jazarī, Ibn ar-Razzāz 10 n.63, 21–23, 24, 25;
    candle-clocks *69*, 118;
    castle water-clock *8*, 22, 23;
    Kitāb fī ma'rifat al-ḥiyal al-handisiya 21–2
Jerome, St., depicted 78 and n.11
Jin Tartars 14, 63

Kaifeng, Su Song's clock at 63
Karnak, clepsydra from *23*, *24*, 1 and n.5, 2 and n.6, 46
Kautiliya-Arthasastra 4 n.23
al-Khāzinī, Abu-l Fatḥ 'Abd ar-Raḥmān al-Man-
    sūr: *Kitāb Mīzān al-Ḥikma* 19 n.113, 20
al-Khuwārizmī, Abu 'Abdallah: *Mafātiḥ al-'Ulūm* 19
Kircher, Athanasius 33
koban dokei, see under Japan
Korea, incense-clocks in 142, 143
Kuhn, H.A. *39*, 68, 72

Laghoda: *Jyotisha-vedangā* 3 n.12, 4 n.23
lamp-clocks *71*, *75–80*, 117, 120–2, 128–39;
    American oil-lamp clock *80*, 138;

in Islam 120 n.10;
  Italian *79*, 136;
  24-hour scale on 130
Lana, Francesco de 122
Lancelloti, Abate 38
Latin: horological treatises lacking in early medi-
  eval period 25;
  translation of Hero 32;
  treatises on astrolabes 28;
  treatises on clepsydrae 29–30, 31;
  treatises on 'planetary instruments' 30
Lebrun, Charles 58
Leo the Philosopher 16
Leontius Mechanicus 16
Lettsom, John Coakley 83 n.35
Leurechon, Jean 33
el-Levi, Samuel: *Libros del Saber 70*, 118–20
Liancourt, Gabry de 122 and n.23
Liang Lingzan 13
literature, technical or horological: Alexandrian 6,
  7, 8, 16, *see also* Hero; Arabic *see below under*
  Islamic;
  Byzantine 15–17, 25; Chinese 12, 14; Egyptian 2
  and n.8;
  Indian 10;
  Islamic 7, 10, 17, 18–22, 25, 30;
  Roman 5, 7–8, *see also* Vitruvius;
  translations of 30, 32–3, 35, 36, 37;
  Western, medieval 30, 31, 37;
  –, Renaissance 35, 37–9
Liutprand of Chartres 76
Liutprand of Cremona 16, 28
Llandaff, Book of 18 n.105
Longitude, English Board of 82
Lorenzetti, Ambrosio, depiction of fresco by 76
Louis IX of France 117
Lucian 8
Ludalin 12 n.76
Lu Ji 13
Lupitus 28
Luther, Martin 100

Mandey, Venturus 121–2
Margaret of York 79
Martinelli, Domenico 39, 82, 121;
  Horologi Elementari 71
Mehmet II, sultan 25 n.131

Mei Ji 142
mercury, as alternative to water in clepsydrae *11*,
  20, 30, 37, 39
M.G.B.H.: *Ausführliche und Vollständige Abhand-*
  lung von Wasseruhren 43
Michael III, Byzantine emperor 16
Michel, Henri 4
Michelangelo 33
models, celestial 7, 8, 9, 12–13, *13*–14, 27, 30; *see*
  also armillary spheres; astrolabes; Su Song
monasteries, clocks in *10*, 25–7, 27 n.140, 30
Moxon, Joseph 122
Muḥammad b.ʿAlī b. Rustam al-Khurāsānī as-Sā-ʿāti 21
Muḥammad al-ʿArabī, Abu ʿAbd Allah 23
Muḥammad b. al-Habbāq at-Tilimasānī, Abu ʿAbd
  Allah 23
Muḥammad (*or* Ahmad) b. Khalaf al-Mūrādī: *Ki-*
  tāb al-asrār 20, 30, 37 n.183
Muḥammad b. Mūsà 18
Muḥammad as-Sinhāgī, Abu ʿAbd Allah 23
Mul Apin texts 3 n.12
al-Muqaddasī 10 and n.62
Mūsā b. Shākir, the Banu 20, 25, 120 n.10;
  Kitāb al-Ḥiyal 19

Nashe, Thomas 35;
  The Unfortunate Traveller 35
Mustanṣirīya College, Baghdad 23
Nāsir ad-Dīn 21
norias 4 n.25, 63;
  see also water-wheels
North Africa, clepsydrae in 4 n.25, 11, 23–4

Oxyrynchus papyri 9, 46 n.210

Pappus of Alexandria 7, 9, 15 n.88, 31 n.163
'parastatic clock' *12*, 6
Paris: Louvre 58;
  Observatory 58
Parisio, Attilio 37–8
Partington, Charles F. 43
Paternus (pilgrim) 18
Patteshall, John 82 n.33
Pearson Page Co., Birmingham 126 and n.24
Peking, Su song's clock at 63
Pencz, G. 78 n.11
Perrault, Charles 58

Perrault, Claude *28, 40–1,* 1 n.1, 36, 43, 56–8, 72; works 58

Persia 11, 15, 17, 18

Peters, Hugh, depicted *46*

Petrie, Sir William Flinders, views on the Edfu clepsydra 50, 52

Petronius 8 n.44

Philip II of Spain 120

Philo of Byzantium 6, 17 n.101, 33

Philoponos, John 15, 16

Pierret, Victor Athanase 122

Place, Francis 81

Plato 6 and n.32

Pliny 7 and n.41

Pogo, A., views on the Edfu clepsydra 50

Polycarp, St. 9

Porta, Giovanni Battista della 33

portolan 78

Proclus: *Hypotyposis* 15

Procopius 9, 18

Prosper, Comte 82

pseudo-Hero 6 n.35

Ptolemy, observations with clepsydra 2, 15 n.88

Qarawiyyin Mosque, Fez 23

Qian Lezhi 13

Quet, M. du 43

Qur'ān 17

Qustà b. Luqà 19

Radi, Archangelo Maria 82

Ramelli, Agostino 35

Ramus, Petrus 35

Raphael, Sanzio 35

Ravenna, clespydra at 28

Rees, A.: *Cyclopaedia 22*

Regiomontanus 32

Ricci, Matteo 14

Richard of Wallingford 27

Ridwān b. Muhammad b. Alī b. Rustam al-Khurā-sānī as-Sā'ātī 9, 21

Rocca, Angelo 38

Roger II of Sicily 25

Rome: clepsydrae at 7; Renaissance automata near 35

St. Alban's Abbey 31

St. Andiol 27

St. Mary's Abbey, Glastonbury 30

Salmon: *l'Art du Potier d'étain 19*

Salmon, Mrs. 121

Salzburg, anaphoric clock dials found at 27 and n.139

sand 75 n.1

sand-clocks: compartmented clylindrical 39 and n.195; literature on 82 n.27

sand-glasses 75–113; astronomical use of 81–2; called dials ('dyolls') in early sources 78 and n.10; dials with 78, 84; domestic use of 78, 81; double-cased *60–2, 66,* 100, 108–9; English *67,* 110–11; English or German *66,* 108–9; fillings for 75 and n.1, 84; French *59, 63–4, 68,* 98–9, 102–3, 104–5, 112–113; French or Italian *65,* 106–7; German *50–2, 54–8,* 86–9, 92–7; invention of 76–8; manufacture of *42–3,* 75–6; maritime use of *45,* 76, 78 and n.12, 81 and n.24, 82, 100; measure specific intervals of time 3, 4, 75, 76, 78, 81; medical use of 83 and n.35; medieval, evidence for *44,* 75, 76; multiple *59, 63–5,* 98–9, 102–7; as pulpit-glasses *46,* 79–81, 81 nn.18–19; refinements of 81, 82–4; scholastic use of *44,* 76, 78; self-turning *49,* 83–4, 84 n.36; sets of *54–8,* 84 and n.38, 92–7; symbolic of death *47–8;* term defined 75 and n.1; term preferred to 'hourglasses' 75 n.1

Sapor, King of Persia 9

Scève, Maurice, quoted 1 and n.1

Schott, Gaspar 33; *Technica Curiosa 16, 20,* 39

Schwenter, Daniel 33

Scipio Nasica 7 and n.41

Sebastian, St. 9

Seneca 8

Sens, clepsydra making at 40

Shāhinshāh-nāma, sand-glasses depicted in 82 n.26

Shen Gua 14

Seth G. Atwood

Founder and Director of The Time Museum, Seth G. Atwood has been a resident of Rockford, Illinois, all his life. He graduated Phi Beta Kappa, with a B.A. in Economics from Stanford University in 1938. He was awarded the M.B.A. from Harvard University Graduate School of Business in 1941 and served with the U.S. Navy from 1942 through 1946. A businessman involved principally in manufacturing and banking, Seth Atwood is the owner of the Clock Tower Inn and The Time Museum. He is a Fellow of the National Association of Watch and Clock Collectors, member of U.S. and English Antiquarian Horological Societies, and member of The International Society for the Study of Time.

Anthony J. Turner

After reading History at Oxford, Anthony Turner concentrated on research in the fields of early scientific instruments, clocks and watches, and the social history of science. He has worked in several museums in Great Britain and is the author of a number of books and articles, including *The Clockwork of the Heavens* (1973); *Scientific Instruments* (1975, with Harriet Wynter); *Science and Music in 18th Century Bath* (1977). He is currently working on a general history of instruments before *c.* 1780. When not engaged in historical research, Anthony Turner organizes exhibitions and is a partner in an antiquarian-book business based in Greenwich (England). He has lived in France since 1979.

Horloge à pendule
qui va par le moyen
de l'Eau.